WHITE LIES

WHITE LIES

DANA ROTBERG • WITI IHIMAERA
SCREENPLAY AND DIRECTOR   ORIGINAL NOVELLA

A SOUTH PACIFIC PICTURES PRODUCTION

VINTAGE

A VINTAGE BOOK published by Random House New Zealand,
18 Poland Road, Glenfield, Auckland, New Zealand

For more information about our titles go to www.randomhouse.co.nz

A catalogue record for this book is available from the National Library of
New Zealand

Random House New Zealand is part of the Random House Group
New York   London   Sydney   Auckland   Delhi   Johannesburg

First published 2013
The novella *Medicine Woman* was first published in *Ask the Posts of the
House* by Reed Books © 2007 Witi Ihimaera
© 2013 Witi Ihimaera & South Pacific Pictures Ltd
The moral rights of the authors have been asserted

ISBN 978 1 77553 306 1
eISBN 978 1 77553 307 8

Photographers: Todd Eyre and Matthew Klitscher
Cover: poster designer Damon Keen; cover designer Megan van Staden
Internal design: Megan van Staden

Printed and bound in Australia by Griffin Press

This publication is printed on paper pulp sourced from sustainably grown
and managed forests, using Elemental Chlorine Free (ECF) bleaching, and
printed with 100% vegetable-based inks.

MIX
Paper from
responsible sources
FSC® C009448

*For John Barnett, who persists in putting
New Zealand stories on screen.*

— WITI IHIMAERA

●

White Lies first appeared under the title of *Medicine Woman* in Witi Ihimaera's collection of five novella-length stories, *Ask the Posts of the House*, published by Reed under its Raupo imprint in 2007. Witi Ihimaera is grateful to Penguin Books for permission to reproduce the original and to use it as the basis for *White Lies*, which has been expanded for the present Random House film edition.

The film script *White Lies — Tuakiri Huna* was written by Dana Rotberg based on the original novella *Medicine Woman* by Witi Ihimaera. Dana wants to thank Kararaina Rangihau, Whitiaua Ropitini and Tangiora Tawhara for the translation to te reo Maori of the dialogue of the film script.

The key stills photographer on *White Lies* was Todd Eyre, and grateful thanks are given to South Pacific Pictures for permission to reproduce them.

CONTENTS

Introduction — John Barnett   8

Acknowledgements — Dana Rotberg   12

WHITE LIES · THE NOVELLA — WITI IHIMAERA   21

WHITE LIES · THE PHOTOGRAPHIC ESSAY — TODD EYRE   97

WHITE LIES · THE SCREENPLAY — DANA ROTBERG   113

From the novella *Medicine Woman* to
  the film *White Lies* — Tuakiri Huna:
  Scriptwriter and director's notes   114

The screenplay   131

WHITE LIES · NOTES AND ORIGINAL NOVELLA
— WITI IHIMAERA   265

Writing the novellas   266

The original novella: *Medicine Woman*   281

WHITE LIES · CAST AND CREW LIST   329

INTRODUCTION

In 2007, I received a call from Rosa Bosch, a friend of mine in London. Rosa, an effervescent, incredibly well-connected film sales agent, had worked with us in bringing *Whale Rider* to the international market. Her expertise in the Hispanic/Latin American market is legendary. She knows every player and all the talent — new and established. She told me that a friend of hers, Dana Rotberg, a film director who had been a leading light in the Mexican film industry in the early 'nineties, had now moved to New Zealand, and we should meet.

One reason that Rosa felt we should meet was to do with Dana's motivation for coming here. Dana and her daughter, Rina, had been living in a small town in Mexico, and by chance they had gone to see *Whale Rider*. The next day, as Rosa told it, Dana decided to move to New Zealand, and, sure enough, here she was, living fifteen minutes away.

Dana and I met and I asked what she wanted to do creatively. She told me she wanted to settle into New Zealand and be a mother to Rina. We talked more, and I said that if she found a project she would like to direct, I'd be happy to assist.

In late 2007, Dana invited me to a party she was having for

her father, who was visiting from Mexico. I took her a book of Witi's short stories, *Ask the Posts of the House*. Some months later, Dana told me that she had found a project and that it was the novella *Medicine Woman*, which was one of the stories in *Ask the Posts*.

Dana took the novella and, in changing and adapting the roles and motivations and the inner qualities of the characters, the film story became a triangle of confronted and conflicting identities.

White Lies, the film version of *Medicine Woman*, would be quite different from the other films I have made. But one theme that captured me was 'identity', and that's something I am interested in. I am interested in how people assert their identity, how they claim it, why they reject it and the consequences of their actions. And I feel that across most nations, cultures, religions, the same elements hold true.

So, for me, *White Lies* is about three characters who are all at different compass points in their connection to their identity: Paraiti, whose beliefs and daily practice are absolutely shaped by her culture; Maraea, who has turned her back on her heritage, culture and people; and Rebecca, who has no knowledge at all of where she comes from. And this triangle is one which has universal resonance.

That was what determined my decision to work with Dana and to adapt Witi's work into the film. Witi tells stories that are universal in their themes and specific in their setting. That approach enables them to reach audiences beyond those who are the subject of his writing.

As we develop our sense of our New Zealandness, we often struggle with issues of 'ownership' of ideas, and there are some who feel that Witi's works, written by a Maori author, mostly set in Maori communities, can only be told by Maori. I do not hold with that any more than I think that only a Scotsman could write *Macbeth*, or a Moor could write *Othello*, or a Jew *The Merchant of Venice*. Our world culture is enhanced by the ideas we ingest from all the experiences we have. When one looks at Roman, Greek, Norse or Polynesian mythologies, we see that each culture has a number of gods whose functions are evident in all the other cultures. The emotions that drive people, their actions and reactions are universal, and that also gives us the connection to seemingly different worlds.

I felt Dana would bring a filter to the adaptation of *Medicine Woman* which would be quite different to that which a local filmmaker might bring. Her experiences in Mexico, and in the Balkans, would give her a take on 'identity' that might make the film accessible beyond the shores of New Zealand. She would tell it from the outside in, rather than the inside out.

And, as with *Whale Rider*, Witi agreed.

So we began the process of adaptation and the eventual production of *White Lies*.

Film production is a journey that often requires the travellers to adapt to circumstances as they change around them. The script and the schedule and the best-laid plans evolve as the production takes place — the exigencies of location, weather, performances, budget and myriad other elements all impact on the process, and the script changes as it moves through the production. The script that is published here is the script of the film that has been delivered and released in cinemas.

As mentioned before, Dana's script and the film were based on Witi's original novella *Medicine Woman*. But just as a film script is a living, breathing entity, so a novel can also change and adapt, and Witi has rewritten the story in his own way, adding scenes, expanding the background and putting in elements in readiness for the sequel he plans to write one day. So, while the original novella is reproduced at the end of this book, what we are showcasing here is how a story can take on new lives, and evolve in different media, with alternative endings and emphases. This book is a celebration of Witi and Dana, and of that creative process.

I am thrilled to say that I think the film Dana has made has realised the aspirations I had for this powerful story.

John Barnett
Producer

ACKNOWLEDGEMENTS

I acknowledge with gratitude all those who made the film *White Lies — Tuakiri Huna* possible (in chronological order):

BOBE TERE-TERESA GOLDSMIT BRINDIS: I made this film in memory of the tears I saw you shed, longing for the true colour of your soul.

RINA KENOVIĆ, my daughter: Because you are the one who inspires me to be a woman of honour and always follow my heart and my dreams. Because in your eyes I find the reason and the purpose for working hard, with honesty, bravery and truth, so we can make a better world for all. For your solidarity, your patience, your always pragmatic advice and for forgiving my absence from your life during the last two years. For helping me translate, revise and correct the many pages I have written for this project from Spanish, my language, to English, your new language.

NIKI CARO: For changing my life with your film *Whale Rider*. Your vision was a profound mirror to the soul of the people and the land. A vision that inspired me to leave Mexico, my homeland, in search of a new life for me and my daughter on this group of tiny and remote islands at the extreme end of the Pacific Ocean: Aotearoa New Zealand.

JIM BUTTERWORTH: For saving my life the first winter I spent in this country, and taking me to hospital in time so I wouldn't die. For being my Kiwi father and my best friend.

ROSA BOSCH and **SHEILA WHITAKER:** For believing that my voice as a filmmaker was still alive, no matter for how many years it had been silent. And for working hard so we can all see this film fly high.

JOHN BARNETT: You took the risk and believed in me, a total stranger with an explosive temperament. And you produced this film, an extreme challenge for all of us, and the most sacred experience I have ever had as filmmaker. I thank you forever.

WITI IHIMAERA: For your *Medicine Woman*, a most beautiful gift.

JON ARVIDSON: For helping me with the English grammar and translation of the synopsis of the script and 'Characters' Journey' document.

MOANA MANIAPOTO: For reading the first synopsis I wrote, only a couple of weeks after Manawanui was born. With tears in your eyes, you encouraged me to make this film.

JULIE PAAMA-PENGELLY: For my ta moko, the creative portal you drew on my right forearm.

JOE MCCLUTCHIE: For your dreams and for guiding my first steps into the Maori culture with your knowledge.

JO JOHNSON: For revising, correcting and improving the very many drafts of the script.

TIM BALME: For your perfect understanding of the language of film and your always precise input in the development of the script.

MINA PRIP and **CALUM MACMILLAN:** For being a family to my daughter and me. For opening the first gate into the Universe of Tuhoe. For crying with me and being happy with me all along the way. For revising the translation in te reo Maori of the script.

ANI PRIP and **HINEIRA WOODARD:** For hosting me in your home in Ruatoki on my first visit to Te Urewera, being patient and generous with me and my infinite ignorance, and for providing us with *Tuakiri Huna*, the perfect title for this film in te reo Maori.

HINEWAI MCMANUS: For sharing with me your brave and generous soul, the soul of a Tuhoe warrior. And for rowing like mad on a windy evening on Lake Waikareiti, so we could get to shelter before dark.

JIM WHITE, RICHARD WHITE and **MERIANN WHITE:** There are not enough words in any language to express the infinite gratitude I feel towards you for welcoming me and this film into your hearts, your whanau and your marae. You shared, with no reservations, the sacred space of Oputao Marae. A humble and beautiful marae, restored and brought to life by a work of love made through the years by Taiwera Ivan White and you, his sons, Richard and Jim. The first wharenui I ever slept in and where, during a long and stormy night, I asked your tipuna for permission to tell this story. It was there I had the honour to be present in the Ringatu ceremony of Te Tekau-ma-rua, and through your mana the idea of the film was presented to the Haahi Ringatu of Ruatahuna and Waikaremoana, asking for their acceptance and blessing. Oputao Marae was the place where we spent long hours discussing the characters of this film and their journey, and we revised the translation of the script into te reo Maori , word by word. It became a production office, a rehearsal studio, the wardrobe-fitting room, a film location. The wairua of Oputao Marae has been a source of strength and inspiration for me. I can only hope that, with this film, it will be honoured as it deserves to be. You are brothers and a sister to me, and without you this film would not exist.

KARARAINA RANGIHAU: You took me by the hand to discover the depth and wisdom of your land and your people. Your knowledge of Tuhoe history and the enormous dignity and pride with which you hold, preserve and protect your identity has been the living expression of mana, something almost forgotten in the world I come from. You have been a ferocious critic when I have been wrong, and I can only thank you for that, and you have been the most generous teacher when I needed to learn. You placed this film in your heart, and you have worked day and night by my side for the last two years to make it happen. Cultural advisor, te reo Maori translator, dialogue coach, casting advisor, location scouter, production and logistics magic wonder woman. Your passion for filmmaking humbles me, and it has been a unique experience and a privilege to know you and to work by your side. Gracias, Camarada.

WHITIAUA ROPITINI: For being the adviser in all matters related to the Ringatu faith and protocols, for the translation of the dialogue in te reo Maori and for representing this film in the Haahi Ringatu of Ruatahuna and Waikaremoana. You spread your enthusiasm for this film all over the valley, and with that you opened the doors and the people's hearts for us.

TANGIORA TAWHARA: You are the Rongoa Wahine. Every day on the set you shared your knowledge of Rongoa, making sure it was represented with respect and integrity. You opened your knowledge to everyone, Pakeha and Maori, and we all became united by that. I thank you for the karakia and for translating to te reo Maori all the dialogues of Paraiti. And for being a supportive and unconditional friend.

HAAHI RINGATU of Ruatahuna and Waikaremoana: You allowed me to be part of your parish, you opened your soul and invited me in. Just to be there and witness the truth and humble sincerity of your spirituality has been the most precious gift I could ever get.

THE PEOPLE OF RUATAHUNA: You embraced this film and made it yours. You welcomed us and shared your homes and your food with us. You worked with us day and night. You lent us props and wardrobe, you gave us advice and took care of us. You were home for us. You are home for me.

KAUMATUA OF HOPURUAHINE: For welcoming us onto your land and allowing us to re-create, for the film, the atrocities committed in the past against your people. Many of you cried when we were shooting those scenes, as you lived again the suffering of your tipuna and the land. It is my hope that, with those tears, some healing may come to your hearts.

TE TUAWHENUA TRUST: For allowing us to film on your land and to take to the screen the amazing beauty of Te Urewera.

MANAWARU TRIBAL EXECUTIVE: For endorsing this film.

CHRIS HAMPSON: For believing in this story, working hard and staying on board until the end of this film. A film that can make us feel proud.

ALUN BOLLINGER: You created a visual universe of exquisite aesthetics. You are an artist who conceives of light and space through the camera frame in a poetic way. You understood the film profoundly and brought it into being with vision, providing the story of our Paraiti, Rebecca and Maraea with a wise sense of compassion and humanity. Your guidance and advice while rewriting the many drafts of the script were crucial.

CHRISTINA ASHER: For the best cast ever.

The amazing three leading actresses: You all brought to the film much more than what I gave you in the script. **WHIRIMAKO BLACK**, you are a brave woman. You brought Paraiti to life with a grounded and sacred quality. **ANTONIA PREBBLE**, for your emotional wisdom, your professional devotion and your profound knowledge of Rebecca, who came from within your skin, to become the unforgettable character we have on the screen. And for gifting us with the narrative of the ending of the film. **RACHEL HOUSE**, you are a powerful, sophisticated and intelligent actress. With those qualities you transformed the villain of our story into a complex and deeply human Maraea.

NANCY BRUNNING: For trusting me.

DEIZHON MANAWANUI KING: Beautiful baby, you are the miracle of this film.

CATHERINE MADIGAN: For your love for films and the endless hours of efficient and perfect work. For the many times you made production miracles. For your vision and support.

STEPHANIE WILKIN: For taking Whirimako Black by the hand with endless generosity.

HAMISH GOUGH: For giving structure to our filming weeks and being the boss.

TRACEY COLLINS: For taking on board the amazing job of re-creating a window to the past of this country, through the production and wardrobe design of the film.

ANDREW BEATTY, VANESSA HURLEY, YOLANDER BARTHAM and **ABBY COLLINS:** For taking over at the last minute the design and production of the challenging make-up of this film. And making it wonderful.

HAYLEY ABBOTT: For trusting I knew my way and for saving me when I didn't.

ADAM MARTIN: For the precision of your suggestions with dialogues of crucial historical and dramatic meaning.

PAUL SUTORIUS: For believing always that we had a beautiful film and for making it flourish in the editing room. For being a good human being.

JOHN PSATHAS: For creating intense, intelligent and emotional music; a bridge that takes the audience to a place where they become one and the same with each one of the characters. With that you brought a new layer of drama into the emotional texture of the film and imprinted a sacred dimension on the story of Paraiti, Maraea, Rebecca and her baby daughter with a refined balance of discretion and passion. For the blessing of your friendship.

RICHARD NUNNS: For the sacred beauty of your taonga puoro.

JAMES HAYDAY: You made a soundscape for this film in which each one of the locations has a voice, a story and a soul. For being up at 4 am on the top of a mountain in the bush of Ruatahuna, freezing cold, recording the first songs of the birds and the sounds of the river. You are a unique creative mind and a loyal colleague. For that you are a dear friend to me.

IMAGES AND SOUND: For always going the extra mile for this film.

EVERY PERSON IN THE CAST AND THE CREW OF THIS FILM: You went with me all the way, not always under easy circumstances, to finish every shooting day with the best possible result. No matter how complicated the challenges were, or the nature of the conflicts we all faced, you brought to the set the best of yourselves to make this film. Its beauty belongs to all of you.

JOHN MACDERMOTT: For being mi buen amigo, and for being a wise and constant source of integrity and goodness.

CAMERON BROADHURST: For your advice, your clarity and your work.

MICK SINCLAIR: For finding the key that unblocked something that can be beautiful.

My friends **CLAIRE STAFFORD, ALI COOMBER, LEANNE POOLEY, PHILIPPA CAMPBELL, CHRIS MEADE, MERCEDES HOPE, MAREE MCDERMOTT** and **LISA WOODS:** For being there for me, when I most needed you.

MY FATHER AND MY MOTHER: For giving me the life I have.

Dana Rotberg

WHITE LIES
THE NOVELLA

WITI IHIMAERA

CHAPTER ONE

Another dawn, and she drags her old bones up from sleep. Her name is Paraiti and when she is sleeping her bones are light and weightless. As she wakes, however, she is aware of all the stiffness, aches and numbness of a body that has aged. She opens her eyes, adjusts to consciousness and listens to her heart thumping away, pushing the blood through thickened veins. 'Still in the land of the living,' she says to herself.

She hears the usual wheeze and gurgle as her lungs force her breath in and out, but there's a lump of phlegm in her throat. 'Aue,' she grumbles as, creaking like an old door on worn-out hinges, she heaves herself into a sitting position. She is wearing a long flannel nightgown buttoned to the neck but, even so, the morning is cold, so she wraps a sleeping blanket around her before opening the flap of the tent and spitting into the cuspidor.

Now that she is awake, Paraiti fumbles under the pillow for her battered and well-thumbed Bible and hymnal. She raises her left hand and starts to chant a karakia, the Lord's Prayer.

'E to matou matua i te rangi,' she begins, 'kia tapu tou ingoa . . .'

Old habits die hard, and Paraiti wouldn't dream of beginning a new day without himene and prayer. Her parents Te Teira and Hera, if they were alive, would roar with laughter to see her now; in the old days, when the faithful were all at karakia in the smoky meeting house, she was the child always squirming and wriggling. 'Kaua e korikori,' Te Teira would reprimand her.

Although Paraiti went for a few years to a native school, she can't read very well; she trusts to her memory when quoting from the Old Testament or singing hymns. She raises her hand again in the sign of the faithful, 'Kororia ki to ingoa tapu, glory be to Thy holy name.' Her religion is Ringatu, created from the narratives of the Old Testament by the Maori prophet, Te Kooti Arikirangi.

Paraiti lifts her eyes to the sky lightening above her, and marvels again at the goodness of God for having made the world and granting her another day to live in it. The huge canopy of native trees has been a protective umbrella for her sleep; the shimmering giant ferns beneath have provided more intimate shelter from the rain. Mist is steaming from the forest, hastening upward in the wind currents that blow it in arabesques and curlicues toward the bright sun. Here, at the bend of a river, with flax and toetoe unfolding in the lower growth, she has had the perfect camping ground.

Morning prayer over, Paraiti whistles out to her stallion, Ataahua, and to Kaihe, her mule. The sound is strong and piercing with an upturned inflection: 'Where are you two?' Well trained, they whinny back. Good, they have not foraged too far away in the night.

Where's Tiaki, her pig dog? Aha, there he is, big and ugly, emerging silently out of the bush on the other side of the river, looking at her. She calls to him, 'Have you brought something for my breakfast or have you been selfish and wolfed it all down yourself?'

No, today Tiaki has been kind to his mistress. He has been hunting and in his jaws is a fat wood pigeon, still alive and unmarked. Even so, he whines, offended that Paraiti should think so ill of him. He jumps headlong into the water, swims across and waits for her to take the bird from his mouth. But he won't let it go.

You can apologise first, mistress.

'Very well,' Paraiti says to him. 'Give me the bird.'

Tiaki sighs, knowing she will release it back into the woods. All his work for nothing?

'Ae, we let this one go. Give the first to Tane, Lord of the Forest.' She kisses the pigeon and gives it freedom; it creaks and whistles its way back into the trees. 'Now go, Tiaki, the second pigeon is for us.'

Paraiti watches her dog bounding back to the river and swimming strongly to the other side, creating a V in the water. Righto, down to the edge, mincing over the pebbles to wash herself, get the pikaru out of her eyes, and use a clean rag to wash her neck, armpits and nether parts. For an old woman, and despite her creaking joints, Paraiti walks with a surprising lightness of step; she is sometimes almost girlish. Where the water laps, she kneels and begins her daily ablutions. While she is at it, she sprinkles some of the drops over her head and looks at her reflection, hoping to see some improvement.

No such luck. Still the same old face, only getting older: big Maori nose, heavy upper lip, lumpy chin, and lots of bushy hair. She fixes the hair by pinning it back with two large ivory combs but, aue, now she can see more of her face. From this angle she looks like a very ugly potato.

'Never mind,' Paraiti says to herself. 'Nobody else around to frighten.'

Time to change into her travelling clothes: layers of blouses all nice and dry, a jerkin made of supple hide, longjohns, a petticoat and long woollen skirt, socks pulled up to the knees and strong boots.

And now, breakfast.

Paraiti rekindles the fire and hangs a billy of water on an iron rod supported by two strong branches; she also puts a skillet among the hot embers.

Tiaki comes back with a second bird.

'It's not the same one we let go, is it?' Paraiti asks. She has a sneaking suspicion that Tiaki has sometimes clipped the bird's wings with his teeth so that it can't fly too far and, when she is not looking, brings the same bird back.

Tiaki ignores her accusation. He drops the pigeon at Paraiti's feet and, now that he has done his duty by his mistress, disdainfully he is off again, this time in search of his own breakfast.

Paraiti plucks the pigeon and puts it in the skillet; very soon it is sizzling in its own fat. From one of her saddlebags she takes some damper bread and manuka honey. There's nothing like a fresh pigeon and damper bread running with manuka honey to soothe the gullet and start the day. A cup of manuka tea is made in the billy and, ka pai, with that extra stimulation to the blood and senses, she is in seventh heaven.

Once she's breakfasted, Paraiti is keen to get going. 'Time to saddle up,' she says.

She puts on a wide-brimmed hat with a string that she ties under her chin. Quickly, she dismantles the tent and bedding and stows them in the saddlebag. She goes down to the river to rinse the breakfast implements, then douses the fire and buries the contents of the cuspidor in the ground. Nobody would ever know she'd been here.

At Paraiti's whistle, Ataahua and Kaihe come at the gallop. She loads Kaihe first, making sure the weight is evenly distributed across his spine — wouldn't want an unbalanced load to endanger the mule as he is climbing the steep slopes — and then she puts the bridle and saddle on Ataahua and taps his knees. Once upon a time she could get on a horse without trouble, but these days it's too much for her old bones.

Ataahua obliges, going down on his front legs. He waits for Paraiti to lift herself aboard and settle, and then hoists himself up with a whinny of grumpiness; over the last few years his mistress has got not only older but heavier. And him? Well, his joints are troubling him too.

'Me haere tatou,' Paraiti tells Ataahua. 'Let us go.'

Pulling her mule after her, Paraiti fords the river at its shallowest crossing; she doesn't want to get wet, but, even so, Ataahua slips into a hole and her hem dips in the water.

Quickly Paraiti shouts, 'Hup!' before the fool horse dumps her completely in the water, and urges him up and onward. Scolding him for not being as young as he once was, she spurs him to climb the track on the other side. Every now and then on the way up she looks behind to check the load on Kaihe.

By the time Paraiti reaches the top of the ridge, Tiaki has joined her with a supercilious look on his face. The mist has lifted from the valleys and the air is clear. The forest is raucous with birdsong. Far away, Paraiti can see the smoke rising above the village of Ruatahuna, her destination.

CHAPTER TWO

Paraiti is not the name she was baptised with.

She was given it when she was six years old and became 'The One with the Blighted Face', for the bright red welt that travels diagonally from her right temple across the bridge of her nose and, luckily missing her left eye, reappears to feather her left cheekbone.

The scar was caused when Paraiti was a young girl, six years old, in 1880. Her parents and other kin were travelling deep within the Urewera country; her father Te Teira was a tohunga, a revered priest and healer, and the other men and women in the group were accompanying him to a Ringatu church service at Ohiwa. One evening, just as they were settling down for the night's meal, they were set upon by constabulary forces who were hunting bigger game — their leader Te Kooti Arikirangi. They recognised Te Teira: although Te Kooti and his followers had put aside their arms, they were still being pursued.

The constabulary restrained Te Teira and the other men with ropes; Hera, Paraiti's mother, had tried too late to take Paraiti into the bush while the forces ransacked the encampment. When the constabulary couldn't find Te Kooti, one of them, a burly menacing man, took a burning branch from the cooking fire. 'Tell me where your leader is,' he shouted at Te Teira.

He was waving the branch so close to Te Teira's face that sparks flew all around him, setting fire to his shirt. Te Teira cried out with terror and fell back onto the ground. The man advanced on him and raised the branch threateningly. 'It will be the worse for you if you do not tell me your leader's whereabouts.'

Te Teira persisted in his pleas: 'I don't know where the prophet is.'

Looking on, Paraiti felt only one desire, to save her father, and she jumped onto the attacker's back to distract his attention.

The man reached behind him, clutched Paraiti and, holding her up by her hair, dangled her before him. 'Is this your cub?' he asked Te Teira. He slashed Paraiti's face with the burning branch and then threw her against the trunk of a tree.

It happened so quickly, but the memory has never left Paraiti in all these years. The pain of the burning. The shock as she slammed into the tree. The pain again, waves of it almost overcoming her. Dazed, she had tried to stand. As her parents and relatives were led away to be imprisoned, Te Teira cried out, 'Daughter, quickly, go to the stream and lie down in the cold water.'

Somehow, Paraiti found the strength to follow his instructions. Her face was on fire as, stumbling, she made her way down the slope to the stream. No sooner had she immersed herself in the water than she fainted.

How long she was unconscious, Paraiti didn't know. Covered in mud, she was found by local Maori who cared for her as her face bubbled and blistered. They applied healing ointments, but there was nothing they could do to reverse the scarring.

A month later, Paraiti left her caregivers and followed the

constabulary, looking for her parents. Having heard that they had been taken to Whakatane to await sentencing, she found them in a small jailhouse. She threw stones through the barred window until they looked out. They were overjoyed to see her but Te Teira grieved to see her face.

Once, she had been such a pretty girl.

'Aue, daughter...'

Paraiti stayed with local Maori, waiting for the circuit judge to arrive to hear the case brought by the constabulary against her parents and her whanau; she visited them every day, squeezing small food delicacies to them through the bars.

At the trial she managed to slip into the courtroom to await her parents' release. Instead Te Teira and Hera were sentenced to two years' imprisonment for taking up arms against the government and were transported by coastal steamer from Whakatane to Auckland. She followed overland and eventually found them again in the Pakeha prison on the outskirts of the boisterous town.

'It is too dangerous for you here,' Te Teira told her. 'Go to Te Kuiti and wait for us there.'

'No,' she said, shaking her head.

Instead, she lived close by the prison in a small squatter settlement with others who had also come to wait out the jail sentence of loved ones. Sometimes she would hear her parents singing comforting songs to her. That is, until the constabulary chased her away.

One day Paraiti witnessed the hanging of one of the faithful. His name was Hamiora Pere, and when the hangman placed the rope over his head he requested that he be given the chance to sing a waiata of farewell. 'Unloose the knot from my throat that I might sing my song,' he said.

His was a terrible death — the sudden fall through the

trapdoor, the crack as his neck snapped. Looking on, Te Teira cried out angrily to Paraiti, 'Now will you go to Te Kuiti? If I am next, I don't want you to see me, lifeless, dangling from the scaffold.'

On her father's instruction, Paraiti therefore joined a band of Te Kooti's followers who were travelling east. A year later Te Teira was finally released. He went straight to Te Kuiti. As soon as father and daughter saw each other, they clasped each other silently. It was there that Te Teira told Paraiti that her mother, Hera, had died in prison. 'There's only you and me now,' he said.

'What shall we do?' Paraiti asked.

'Go on living,' he answered, 'and do what we have always done: serve God and the people.'

He resumed his calling as a tohunga, preaching the gospel and working as a healer among the morehu, the followers of Te Kooti.

From that moment, they were never apart.

●

On this first day of June, in the Year of Our Lord, 1935, Paraiti is sixty-one years old and the land wars between Pakeha and Maori have been over for some forty years. Although she has not succeeded her father as a tohunga, Paraiti has continued his work as a traditional healer. Modern medical services may now be available in the many towns and cities that have sprung up around Aotearoa, but Maori in the backblocks and remote coastal areas still rely on their traditional medicine men and women. How can they afford the Pakeha doctors during these years of the Depression?

A few weeks ago, Paraiti was still in her village of Waituhi, in Poverty Bay, where she had settled during the second decade of the twentieth century. At the height of the terrible Spanish influenza epidemic of 1918, when the Four Horsemen of the Apocalypse reaped a rich harvest among Maori, Te Teira had received a plea for help from a powerful kuia of Waituhi. Her name was Riripeti and she was setting up a hospital to cater for the ill and dying, but she needed people with medical skills to staff it.

Paraiti was then forty-four, and Te Teira had implicit trust in her. 'I have to stay here, daughter. You must go to Riripeti in my place.' Obeying her father, Paraiti set off for Waituhi. As soon as she saw the valley, with its sacred mountain at one end and ancient fortress at the other — and the sparkling Waipaoa River running through it — she knew this would not be a temporary visit. Her sense of wonder mounted when she saw Riripeti's canvas hospital, which people called Te Waka o Te Atua, The Ship of God, because when the tents were erected they looked like sails.

And then Paraiti saw the valley's great meeting house, Rongopai, holding up the sky. Word of its fame had already circulated among the faithful, but even so, she was unprepared for its holiness. It was indeed a cathedral to the vision of the prophet, Te Kooti, so beautifully decorated and carved that she felt, on first entering it, that the angel who guarded it had sheathed his golden sword and let her into the Garden of Eden. The walls were like tall trees, elaborately painted in greens, blues and reds; she was wrapped in the glow of an illuminated forest. Through the branches flew fantastic birds, such species as were dreamed of in Paradise. And the Maori ancestors were everywhere, standing, running, climbing through this world before the Fall.

It was only a matter of time before she returned to stay.

●

The autumn was unseasonably cold in 1935 when Paraiti began preparing for her travels from Waituhi. The southerlies had driven into the foothills where she now lived in a two-room kauta close to the meeting house.

No matter the bitter weather, Paraiti was determined to keep to her seasonal trip as ordained by the Maori calendar — and the Maori New Year, Matariki, was imminent. Also, she had become stir-crazy and wanted to be out on the road.

After all, the people were waiting.

From her stockpile of medicines Paraiti carefully selected the small bottles and tins of ointments, philtres and lotions she thought she would need for the various village clinics, wrapping them separately for her saddlebags so that they wouldn't clink or clang on the journey. Most of her medicines, however, she would gather fresh from the special secret places in the forest and along the coast, among them rimu gum for haemorrhaging, the mamaku pith for scrofulous tumours, seaweed for goitre and pirita for epilepsy.

For personal provisions she took only kao, dried kumara and water. Food would be her payment from her patients, and, should she require extra kai for herself and her animals, as always, the Lord and the land would provide: fern grounds, pa tuna, taro and kumara gardens and bird sanctuaries.

Paraiti took a small tent and a bedroll. For protection she put her rifle in a sling and a knife in her left boot. Although she might not be attractive, she was still a woman, and men were men.

She went to Rongopai to pray for safekeeping on her journey — surely there was no better place to set out from than this testament to the resilience of the people. Then she filled five blue bottles with the healing waters that bubbled from a deep underground spring behind the house, and sprinkled herself and her animals with the water.

Finally, Paraiti strapped the saddlebags around Kaihe's girth, bridled and saddled Ataahua, got him to kneel as usual and climbed on. 'I know, I know,' she said to the horse as she straddled him, to stop his usual irritation. Straightaway, she urged him up: 'Timata.'

She whistled to Tiaki to follow her. 'Don't fall too far behind,' she called as she headed Ataahua into the foothills behind Waituhi.

As she passed by the houses of the village, people looked out and sighed, 'Good, the old lady is on her way with her travelling garden. All's right with the world.' Every season without fail, the takuta was always about her work among the people; this season, the star cluster of Matariki was already gleaming in the night heaven.

A day's ride took Paraiti to the boundary between the lands of Te Whanau a Kai and Tuhoe, and there she sought Rua's Track, one of the great horse trails joining the central North Island to the tribes of Poverty Bay in the east. She followed the track up the Wharekopae River, through Waimaha by way of the Hangaroa Valley to Maungapohatu. Once upon a time there had been such a thriving community there, the holy citadel of Rua Kenana, another great prophet; survivors were still living within the mists of the mountain, waving at Paraiti as they scrabbled among their plantations, eking a living from the land.

Those who travelled Rua's Track were mainly Maori like Paraiti herself; sometimes they were families, but most often they were foresters, labourers or pig hunters.

On her third day, she joined a wagon train of some forty people travelling in the same direction. 'E hika,' they jested. 'Is the forest moving?' Her saddlebags were overflowing with her herbal supplies. 'Oh, it's just you, Paraiti. E haere ana koe ki hea? Where are you going?'

Paraiti was a familiar sight and they were honoured to have her with them. She, in turn, valued the opportunity to sharpen up her social skills, to share a billy of manuka tea and flat bread, to spend time playing cards and to korero with some of the old ones about the way the world was changing. But the wagon train made slow progress, so Paraiti took her leave and journeyed on alone.

'Ma te Atua koutou e manaaki,' she called in farewell.

And now, Ruatahuna lay ahead.

CHAPTER THREE

Paraiti notices that Tiaki's ears have pricked up. The dog looks at her: Are you deaf, mistress?

Then, even she hears the high tolling of a bell coming from Ruatahuna. 'Ka tangi te pere,' she nods. 'I know, Tiaki, we will be late for the service.'

The bell rings at the meeting house, Te Whai a Te Motu, calling the Ringatu faithful to gather together on this very special day. In the church calendar the first of June is the Sabbath of the Sabbath and the beginning of the Maori New Year, with the pre-dawn rising of Matariki, the bright stars of fruitfulness. On this happy day, each person contributes seeds to the mara tapu, the sacred garden, for out of the seed comes the new plant, symbolic of the renewal of God's promise to all his people.

Paraiti urges Ataahua quickly through the village: most of the houses are drab weatherboard with tin roofs, but a few are brightly painted. Some of the local dogs bark at them, and Paraiti gives Tiaki a warning glance. 'Don't bark back, it's Sunday.' He gives her a sniffy look, then growls menacingly at the dogs so that they whine and back away. They know Tiaki from past visits to Ruatahuna: he never retreats. Indeed, it was for this quality that Paraiti chose him when a pig hunter, whom she treated for a shoulder torn apart by a boar, offered one of his newborn litter of pups as payment. She had the thought that a dog would provide extra protection for her so she agreed to the offer. Putting out her hand, she watched the pups scrambling to reach it, and saw the runt pushing his other bigger siblings away — and then he held her gaze and bit her finger, drawing blood.

'Well,' she said, 'if you want the job that much, you have it.'

Ahead, Paraiti sees her cousin Horiana's house; it is one of the brightly painted ones. She knows Horiana won't mind if she ties the animals to her fence. 'Don't eat Horiana's roses,' she tells Kaihe. Even so, she is troubled to see that the roses are taking over the native vines in the garden.

Wrapping her scarf around her face, and taking with her a small sachet of seeds, Paraiti makes for the marae. Horses and buggies are tethered to the fence outside and, hello, a few motoka are parked there as well. She walks through the carved gateway, stands a moment before the meeting house, remembering the dead and paying homage to it, and then crosses the threshold of the porch to peer inside the whare.

The atmosphere inside is smoky and dark, but there's no doubting that it is packed with locals. People are sitting up against the walls, prayer books in hands. Wirepa, the local poutikanga, pillar of authority, is leading the service. He is about the same age as Paraiti, and he gives a brief nod in her direction.

Paraiti unlaces her boots, takes them off and slips through the door of the meeting house.

'Kororia ki to ingoa tapu,' Wirepa intones. 'And verily, an angel appeared to the prophet Te Kooti, and the angel was clothed in garments as white as snow, his hair like stars, and he wore a crown and a girdle like unto the setting sun and the rising thereof, and the angel's fan was like the rainbow and his staff was a myriad hues. And the angel said to Te Kooti, "I will not forsake thee or my people either." And so we prevail to this very day. Glory be to Thy holy name. Amine.'

Paraiti sees Horiana beckoning and making a place beside her. Stooping, she makes her way over to her cousin; some of the worshippers recognise her and smile or hold out their hands for her to clasp as she passes.

'E noho, whanaunga,' Horiana welcomes her. They kiss and hug as if they haven't seen each other for a thousand years. 'We'll korero afterwards,' Horiana whispers, opening her prayer book.

Paraiti gives a sign of apology to Wirepa for interrupting the service. She removes her scarf and hears a buzz as people who hadn't seen her entering realise she has arrived — 'Scarface ... Te takuta ... The doctor ... Blightface.' She smiles at familiar friends. She doesn't mind that people call her Scarface or Blightface; they use the name as an identification, not to mock her.

She lets herself be absorbed into the meeting house. It is such an honour to be sitting within Te Whai a Te Motu, with its figurative paintings and beautiful kowhaiwhai rafter patterns. Here, in the bosom of this holy place, Paraiti joins in praising and giving thanks to God.

When the service is over, the people adjourn to the mara tapu outside, where Paraiti and others offer their seeds for the sowing. Wirepa intones a final karakia. Then there are people to be greeted and further korero to be had with the local elders.

'You will set up your tent in the usual place?' Wirepa asks.

'Thank you, rangatira,' Paraiti answers.

'Time to get started,' Paraiti says to Horiana, after the midday meal. She can already see that people are waiting to see her.

Nodding, Horiana yells to some young boys, 'Go and get the takuta's tent, eh?' They run to Kaihe and unload the medicinal supplies; once the tent is up they arrange a makeshift stretcher inside and then hold out their hands for some liquorice they have seen when unpacking the supplies.

Horiana is Paraiti's assistant in Ruatahuna and has been taking bookings. 'Lots of people want to see you,' she tells her, as she shouts to the boys again, this time ordering them to bring some chairs from the meeting house for the old people so that they don't have to stand. 'The usual problems,' Horiana continues. 'Nothing too difficult so far.' Horiana is very proud of the status that Paraiti's visits give her. 'I could have handled most of the cases myself,' she adds.

Always bossy, Horiana sits outside the tent deciding who should enter and depart. Inside, the patients and their wives, husbands or partners sit on the chairs or lie on the stretcher: a slab of wood covered with a finely woven flax mat. Stacked against one of the walls of the tent are the rongoa and the herbal pharmacy that Paraiti draws on for her work. Not all have been brought by her; some have been stockpiled by Horiana for her arrival. On a small table are the surgical implements of her trade. Unlike some of her brother and sister healers, Paraiti shuns Pakeha utensils and keeps to traditional ones: wooden sticks and scrapers, sharp-edged shells and obsidian flakes for cutting, thorns for opening up abscesses, and stones to heat before placing on the body.

Major bone setting requires steam treatment, so Paraiti organises times at a makeshift spa. Her father had been renowned for his skill with massage, a special knowledge instilled in him by his mother, and he passed on to his daughter the techniques to heal and knit broken bones. He also taught her therapeutic massage for the elderly; he himself loved nothing better than to submit himself to Paraiti's strong kneading and stroking of his body to keep his circulation going.

'Daughter,' he would sigh, 'you have such goodness in your hands.'

The clinic opens and most patients are easily diagnosed — those with coughs or colds are treated with houhere and tawa; children with asthma or bronchitis are given kumarahou. Boils are lanced and the ripe cores squeezed out before Paraiti returns the patient to Horiana to apply a strong and tensile spider-web poultice.

Paraiti gives a short greeting to patients returning for check-ups, and notes whether a broken leg has set well, or a burn is in need of further treatment with harakeke and kauri gum. Sprained joints are treated with weka oil or kowhai juice; with Horiana holding the patient, Paraiti eases the joint back in place, then instructs Horiana how to bind it.

A young man with a deep cut on his forehead comes in. 'How did you come by that?' Paraiti asks.

'His wife threw a knife at him when he came home drunk from the hotel,' Horiana answers, rolling her eyes with contempt.

'Perhaps it is her I should be treating,' Paraiti says lightly as she applies rimu gum to the wound.

Horiana is adamant. 'No, it's him who's the problem,' she answers.

'You will need stitches,' Paraiti says. She makes a thread of muka and uses a wooden needle to sew the skin together. As a dressing, she applies the ash from a burnt flax stalk. Throughout all this, the young man does not flinch. He's a cheeky one, though; just before he leaves he asks, 'Scarface, you couldn't throw in a love potion with the treatment, could you? My wife's still angry with me and won't let me perform my customary and expert lovemaking duties.'

Paraiti's eyes twinkle. 'Oh really? I have heard otherwise about your lovemaking. Do you think it might be the beer that is putting you off your stroke? No love philtre is required. Your wife will eventually forgive you and soon you will plough her in your usual diligent and boring manner, the poor woman. But if you must drink, chew puwha gum — it will mask your breath when you go home at night.'

Another young man comes in, but, as soon as he sees Paraiti, he changes his mind and goes out. He is embarrassed because he has a venereal disease. Then a young woman with shell splinters in the heels of her feet requires a little more care; she carelessly ran across a reef while gathering pupu and mussels. 'I was being chased by a giant octopus,' she tells Paraiti.

Paraiti winks at Horiana. 'Oh yes, and what was his name?' She cuts around the wound until the pieces of shell can be seen. Smiling at the young woman, Paraiti then lowers her head. 'Here is the kiss of Scarface,' she says. She bites on each piece of shell and pulls it out. 'If your octopus really loves you and wants to ensnare you in his eight arms, and if that causes you to run over shells again, show him how to use his own teeth.'

The next patient causes some hilarity. He has constipation and hasn't had a good bowel movement for days. 'I have just the right potion,' Paraiti tells him. 'Crushed flax roots and, here, if you disrobe, I will also blow some potion into your rectum so that the result comes quicker.'

But the patient's wife is with him. 'Oh no, you don't! If anybody is to disrobe my husband and blow anything up his rectum, it will be me! Do I want the whole world to know how awful a sight his bum is? Best for him and me to keep that treasure a family secret.'

So it goes on throughout the remainder of the day; each patient pays Paraiti in coin or in food — a koha, no matter how small. However, there are some who lack obvious symptoms and whose treatment cannot be diagnosed with ease. With such patients Paraiti takes a history of their activities before they became ill and, if she suspects an answer, administers a likely remedy: harakeke to cleanse the blood, kaikaiatua as an emetic or huainanga to expel tapeworms. If she is still unsure, and if the person has a temperature, she advises them to drink lots of clean water and gives them a herbal mixture which will alleviate the pain or combat their fever. 'Sometimes,' she tells them, 'the body has its own way of making itself well again. Time will tell.'

There are other patients whom Paraiti will treat separately, away from the clinic at Horiana's house, because their conditions are more serious. One is a young girl with an eye condition that bespeaks oncoming blindness. A second is an old koroua with a debilitating illness; nothing can cure old age, but, as she often did with her father, Paraiti will give this old man a good massage and a steam bath for temporary relief. He is already walking towards God.

The time comes to stop work for the day. 'Come back tomorrow,' Horiana tells the other people waiting in line. They are disappointed, but another day won't hurt them.

'But I will see the mother,' Paraiti says, pointing to a woman waiting with her daughter. She has constantly given up her place in the line to others.

'Thank you, takuta,' the mother says respectfully as she steps into the tent. She is trying to hide her distress. 'Actually, I do not come for my own sake but on behalf of my daughter, Florence. Do you have something that will enable her to keep her baby? She can never go to term and loses the baby always around the third month.'

Paraiti notices how small Florence is. She places her hands on the girl's stomach. E hika, this girl is very cold. 'How many times have you conceived?' Paraiti asks her.

'Three,' Florence replies, 'and three times my babies have died inside me. But I really want this child.'

Paraiti takes a look at the girl. She smells her breath; aue, she smokes the Pakeha cigarettes. She looks at her eyes; they are milky and clouded, and her fingernails and toenails are brittle and dry. Finally, Paraiti feels with her fingers around the girl's womb — again, so cold. She speaks, not unkindly, to the girl.

'A baby in the womb is like a kumara being fed nutrients from the vine of your body. But your vine is not giving your baby the right foods. Your circulation is sluggish and, therefore, the nourishment is not getting to the child. Bad foods and bad vine are the reasons why, in the third month, your baby withers and dies. Also, the garden in which your baby grows is not warm.'

Paraiti looks at Florence's mother. 'I will put your daughter on a diet, which she must follow without straying from it,' she tells her. 'The diet is rich in nutrients. I will also put her on a regime of exercise that will improve her circulation. Florence must stop smoking Pakeha cigarettes immediately. Also, it is important that her blood temperature is increased. I will show you a special massage to make her body a whare tangata that is nice and cosy. Keep to the diet, the massages, and encourage your daughter to spend as much time as possible in the sunlight. Make sure she eats vegetables and fruits and fish, especially shellfish.'

The mother holds Paraiti's hands and kisses them. 'Thank you, takuta.'

Paraiti sees them to the flap of the tent. 'I will also give you some herbs that will improve Florence's health while she is with child.'

'Will you attend the birth?' the mother asks.

'No,' Paraiti answers. 'The authorities will not allow it.' She turns to Florence. 'Go well, and be assured that if you follow my instructions, the birth should be normal and you will be delivered of a healthy child.' She kisses Florence on the forehead. 'What greater blessing can any woman have than to give birth to a son or daughter for the iwi? Will you let me know when the baby is born? Ma te Atua koe e manaaki.'

This is Paraiti's world. Dedicated to the health of the people, she is a giver of life. But recently she has been presented with a dilemma.

As she closes her clinic in Ruatahuna for the day, her thoughts fly back to a request she received just before leaving Waituhi.

She was asked to take life, not to give it.

CHAPTER FOUR

This is how the request happened.

In the middle of packing for her annual trip, a thought popped into Paraiti's head: 'I think I'll ride into Gisborne and go to the pictures.' Just like that the thought came, and the more she pushed it away, the more it pushed back: be kind to yourself, mistress, take a day off.

Truth to tell, Paraiti didn't need an excuse to go, so she made one up: she would buy some gifts for all the women who would be helping at her clinics on her travels. Horiana wasn't the only one, but for Horiana especially she would get her some of those Pakeha bloomers that would keep her nice and cool in the summer.

Paraiti got up at the crack of dawn, dressed in her town clothes, saddled Ataahua and, with Tiaki loping ahead, set off for Gisborne. She stopped for a picnic lunch by the Taruheru River, watching as cattlemen approached, herding a new breed of Pakeha cows along the side of the river: farms were springing up quickly, the settlers hastening to take advantage of the rich pasture land. Then she realised, e hika, that she didn't want to complete her journey riding in the wake of the herd's dust and smell of cow shit. Time to move on.

She rode on along the riverbank to Gisborne and settled her horse in the municipal stables at the Peel Street bridge. The town lay spread out on the other side, under the watchful eye of Kaiti Hill, as the Pakeha called the maunga now. It was midday by the town clock when she joined the townsfolk on Gladstone Road.

Paraiti always came to Gisborne with some apprehension. It was a bustling country town, with shops, clothing emporiums and a couple of picture theatres all gathered in a four-block stretch along Gladstone Road, from the small port to the clock tower itself. The citizens were mainly Pakeha, but there were a few Maori around the usual watering holes: the hotels and billiard parlour.

Being among Pakeha was not natural for her; she felt she was crossing some great divide from one world to another. The slash of the scar across her face didn't help either, since it marked her out in some sinister way. Even though these were modern times, and Pakeha liked to say that Maori and Pakeha were one people now, there were still signs of division: there were the Pakeha parts of Gisborne, particularly the palatial houses along Waterside Drive, and then there were the narrow shanty streets where the Maori lived.

Steadying her nerves, Paraiti made her way along the main street. The town was busier than usual. A general election was to be held at the end of the year and, already, members of the United and Reform parties were out, touting for votes: 'Vote Forbes for Prime Minister,' they cried. Not to be outdone, the rival Labour Party countered with shouts of 'Michael Joseph Savage, he's the man to vote for.' They had even brought along some highland dancers to entertain the crowd.

Paraiti pushed through the throng to the Regent picture theatre to see what film was on. Although talkies had arrived a few years ago, she was delighted to see that Charlie Chaplin's silent film *The Gold Rush* was showing: 'Returns to the Screen by Popular Demand.' She bought a ticket at the booth.

Humming to herself, Paraiti looked at the town clock again and saw that she had an hour to wait before the film began — time enough to go shopping. As she crossed Gladstone Road to Harrison's Haberdashery, the latest model Packard went by with two women in it. The car was shiny, gleaming black, with every silver door handle and piece of trim polished to perfection. Driving the car was a young Pakeha woman with auburn hair; she was of considerable beauty, wearing a smart cloche hat and smoking a cigarette. Beside her was a middle-aged Maori woman, probably her maid. When the Maori woman saw Paraiti her eyes widened — she looked again and pointed Paraiti out to her mistress.

Paraiti entered Harrison's and went over to look at the bolts of fabric. Despite the hard times the shop was filled with laces, silks, wools, calicoes, twills and cottons for those who could afford it. A senior saleswoman appraised her as she came in and immediately approached her.

'May I help you?' she asked.

There was no accompanying 'Madam' to her enquiry, but Paraiti had been to Harrison's before and knew the kawa, the protocol:

1. Shop attendants were always supercilious but they were, sorry lady, only shop assistants, even if they were senior.
2. She had as much right as anyone else to shop in Harrison's.
3. Her money was as good as anybody's.

She unpinned her hat and placed it on the counter, claiming some territory. 'Why, thank you,' she said pleasantly, articulating the words in a clear, clipped accent. She had learnt by experience that one of the best ways of getting on in Pakeha society was to speak like they did; self-taught, she could now hold her own in English against any policeman, person of authority or, as in this case, supercilious shop attendant. And if that didn't work . . .

Paraiti revealed her scar in order to intimidate the saleswoman; sometimes it came in handy. 'I'd like to see that bolt of cloth and that one and that one,' she said, pointing to fabrics that were highest in the stacks.

The saleswoman looked as though she would like to gag; she was only too happy to get away.

Good, that would keep the nuisance busy for a while.

Paraiti rummaged through some of the other fashionable material and accessories that were on display. By the time the saleswoman got down from two ladders, she had made her selection: a variety of attractive lengths of fabric, bold, with lots of flash. She also selected a couple of pairs of bloomers with very risqué ruffles on the legs. 'Would you be so kind as to wrap all this,' Paraiti asked as she paid for her purchases, 'and I will collect the parcels at four at the latest.'

Avoiding looking at her scarred customer, the saleswoman nodded quickly — but Paraiti was not about to let her off the hook yet. Pleased with herself, she waited at the doorway for the saleswoman to observe the final piece of kawa in any commercial transaction:

4. When the paying customer is ready to depart, the door is always opened for her.

In a happy mood, Paraiti made her way back to the Regent. She was humming to herself as she entered the opulent foyer, with its gold cherubs and beautiful carpet and sweeping staircase. As she took her seat, the Maori maid, who had alighted from the Packard and had been watching Paraiti in the haberdashery, found a place a few rows back.

A man at the piano began to play 'God Save the King' and

everyone stood to pay their respects to the sovereign. Then the audience settled to watch the first half: a short travelogue on India and a news digest.

Paraiti loved nothing better than to sit in the dark where nobody could see her, and get caught up in the fantasies on the screen. During the interval she treated herself to some chocolates and looked at the posters and lobby cards that lined the walls of the foyer. A talking movie was being advertised as a forthcoming attraction: *The Private Life of Henry VIII* starring Charles Laughton and 'Alexander Korda's sensational new star, Miss Merle Oberon'. She caught sight of the Maori maid and gave a brief nod. The house lights were dimming as she returned to her seat. With anticipation she watched as the grand blue satin curtains rose and *The Gold Rush* began; the Maori maid moved closer.

Paraiti had seen Charlie Chaplin's previous movie, *The Kid*, and hoped that *The Gold Rush* would be just as good — and it was; it was even better. Paraiti thought she would die of laughter — the tears were running down her face at the part where the starving man kept looking at the little tramp and imagined seeing a nice juicy chicken. And she just about mimi-ed herself when the little tramp was in the pivoting hut caught on the edge of a crevasse; the hut see-sawed whenever Charlie walked from one side to the other. At the end, the entire audience clapped like mad: Charlie Chaplin was the greatest film clown in the world. Paraiti was so glad that she had come to town, but when she came out of the theatre into the mid-afternoon sun and saw the Maori maid standing in the sunlight like a dark presence, she felt as if somebody had just walked over her grave.

'You are Scarface?' the maid asked. She was subservient, eyes downcast, her years weighing her down — but her words were full of purpose. 'May I trouble you for your time? I have a mistress who needs a job done. If you accept the job, you will find the price to your liking.'

Although everything in her being shouted out, 'Don't do this, turn away', Paraiti equivocated. She had always believed in fate, and it struck her that coming to Gisborne might not be coincidental; and, after all, this maid was a Maori. She found herself saying, 'Kei te pai, all right. Let me pick up my parcels from the haberdashery and drop them off at the municipal stables and then I will give your mistress an hour of my time.'

That task accomplished, the Maori servant introduced herself. 'My name is Maraea,' she said. 'My mistress is Mrs Rebecca Vickers. The Honourable Mr Vickers is currently in Europe on business. My mistress and I are only recently returned to Gisborne from England. Mr Vickers has been detained in London but is due to return soon. Be good enough to follow me, but stay far enough back so that people do not know that we are together.'

Paraiti was immediately offended, but it was too late — she had already agreed to the appointment. She followed Maraea away from the din of the crowded town into the private Pakeha part of Gisborne: not many people were about except for the occasional passing cars, their occupants too sophisticated to notice two Maori women walking along the suburban pavement.

'We are almost there,' Maraea said as she led Paraiti around a corner and onto Waterside Drive. Here the elegant houses, most of them Edwardian, two-storeyed, faced the river where willow trees were greening along the banks. 'The Vickers' residence is the fourth house along, the big one with the rhododendron bushes and the wrought-iron gate. When we arrive at the house I will go in and see if it is safe for my mistress to see you. Kindly do not approach until I signal to you with my handkerchief.'

What have I got myself into? Paraiti wondered. Increasingly irritated, she watched Maraea walk towards the house, disappear and, after a minute or so, return to the street and wave her handkerchief. Paraiti approached and was just about to go through the gate when she heard Maraea whisper from the bushes: 'Do not come in through the front entrance, fool. Go around to the side gate. I will open the back door for you.'

Paraiti obeyed and walked along the gravelled pathway. A Maori gardener at work in the garden tipped his hat to her. She recognised him as a Ringatu follower who lived on a nearby marae, and inclined her head. Maraea stood at the doorway to the kitchen.

'Come in,' she urged Paraiti. 'Quickly now. And you,' she said to the gardener, 'Mrs Vickers is not pleased with the way you have trimmed the lawn. Do it again.'

Paraiti followed Maraea down a long corridor to the front of the house.

The sun shone through the stained-glass panels of the front door. The entrance hall was panelled with polished wood, and a Persian carpet covered the floor; the atmosphere was silent and heavy. A tall mahogany grandfather clock stood against one wall and a huge oval mirror hung on another. There was a small table with a visitors' book, and a vase of chrysanthemums in the curve of the stairway. Hanging from the ceiling was a crystal chandelier.

'Please take off your hat,' Maraea instructed.

Paraiti looked up. Above the first landing was a large painting framed in gold of a lovely woman with red hair and blue eyes, dressed in an exquisite lace ball gown of an earlier generation; elegantly posed against a sylvan landscape, she was demure and sweet of smile. 'Mrs Vickers' mother,' Maraea said, as she ushered Paraiti into the living room. 'Lady Sarah Chichester. She was beautiful, was she not?'

●

'Come away from the window.'

Paraiti had been waiting a good ten minutes before Mrs Vickers arrived. The room had all the trappings and accoutrements required by prosperous Pakeha gentry. The rich green velvet curtains were held back with gold tassels. Damask-covered antique chairs were arranged around small card tables; in front of one window was a charming chaise longue. The furnishings had an Oriental look — as if the Vickers had spent some time in the East — and indeed on the mantel above the fireplace was a photograph of a smiling couple, a young wife with her older husband, standing with an Indian potentate. Electric lights with decorative glass lampshades were set into the walls, and everywhere there were mirrors. Paraiti had gravitated to a window, wishing very much to open it and let some air in, and was looking out at the garden.

Turning, she immediately became disoriented; the hairs prickled on the back of her neck. In all the mirrors a young woman was reflected — she looked like the painting on the landing come to life. She was in her late twenties, with red, hennaed hair, tall and slim, and wearing a simple crêpe de Chine dress in soft shades of green. Which was the woman and which was her reflection? And how long had she been standing there?

On her guard, Paraiti watched as the woman approached her. As had been obvious when she drove past, she was pale, beautiful. Her skin was powdered to perfection; her eyes were green, flecked with gold, the irises large and mesmerising and full. Paraiti resisted the hypnotic gaze, and immediately the woman's irises narrowed. Then she did something strange — almost seductive. She cupped Paraiti's chin, lifted her face and clinically observed, then touched, the scar.

The act took Paraiti's breath away. Nobody except Te Teira had ever been so intimate with her.

'I was told you were ugly,' the woman said in a clipped

English accent, though not without sympathy. 'But really, you are only burnt and scarred.' She withdrew her hands, but the imprint of her fingers still scalded Paraiti's skin. Then she turned, wandering through the room. 'My name is Rebecca Vickers,' she said. 'Thank you for coming. And if you have stolen anything while you have been alone in the room, it would be wise of you to put it back where it belongs before you leave.'

Paraiti bit back a sharp retort. She tried to put a background to the woman: a well-bred English girl of good family, married to a man of wealth who travelled the world, accustomed to a household run by servants. She clearly regarded Paraiti as being on a similar social level to her maid. But there was also a sense of calculation, as if she was trying to manoeuvre Paraiti into a position of subservience, even of compliance.

'What might I help you with, Mrs Vickers?' Paraiti asked. She saw that Maraea had come into the room with a small bowl of water, a flannel and a large towel.

'Thank you, Maraea.' Casually, with great self-possession, Rebecca Vickers began to unbutton her dress; it fell to the floor. Her skin was whiter than white, and without blemish. Aware of her beauty, she stepped out of the garment, but kept on her high heels. Although she was wearing a silk slip, Paraiti immediately saw what her artfully designed clothes had been hiding: Mrs Vickers was pregnant. 'It's very simple,' she said, as she removed her underwear 'I'm carrying a child. I don't want it. I want you to get rid of it.'

Her directness stunned Paraiti. She recognised the battle of wills that was going on. Mrs Vickers was obviously a woman used to getting her way, and there was nothing to stop Paraiti from leaving except that sense of fate; she would bide her time and play the game. 'Would you lie on the sofa, please,' she said brusquely.

'Oh?' Rebecca Vickers laughed. 'I was expecting at least some questions and, surely, just a little . . . resistance.'

'My time is precious,' Paraiti answered as she began her examination, 'and I doubt whether you are worth my trouble.' She did not bother to warm her hands, and was pleased to see the younger woman flinch at their coldness. 'When did you last menstruate? How many weeks have passed since then?' she asked as she felt Mrs Vickers' whare tangata — her house of birth — to ascertain the placement of the baby and the point the pregnancy had reached. The uterus had already grown to the height of the belly-button, and the skin was beginning to stretch.

Paraiti concluded her inspection. Mrs Vickers liked to be direct and was expecting . . . resistance . . . was she? Time then to be direct, to be resistant and push back. 'You are a Pakeha,' she began. 'Why have you not gone to a doctor of your own kind?'

'Of course I have consulted European doctors,' Rebecca Vickers answered somewhat scornfully, 'and much earlier than this when I realised I was pregnant. Whatever they did to me did not work.'

'Then why have you not had further consultations with them?' Paraiti asked.

'Don't think that I haven't done what you suggest. Just before returning to New Zealand from England I even consulted a back-street abortionist, a butcher who failed in his job. And now no doctor will do what I ask, considering that I've gone beyond the point of no return. But when Maraea saw you in the street today she thought you might offer me some hope. She told me that you Maori have ancient ways, and could get rid of it.'

'If your doctors cannot perform your miracle for you,' Paraiti flared, 'don't expect me to be able to. Oh yes, I know of herbs that can end the pregnancy, but they work only in the first nine weeks. However your baby is at least double that — too late for the herbs that will make your uterus cramp and break down, so that the baby can be expelled from the womb.'

Angrily, Rebecca Vickers put on her dress again. 'I knew

this was a foolish notion, but Maraea told me that you especially were renowned for your clever hands and that, by manipulation, you could secure the result I seek.'

'You assumed I would do it just because you asked me?' Paraiti's voice overrode the other woman's. When she had been examining Mrs Vickers the baby had *moved*, cradling against Paraiti's palms, almost as if it knew Paraiti was there, trying to snuggle in. And oh, Paraiti's heart had gone out to it. 'Why are you intent on ridding yourself of your baby? Most women would be overjoyed to be a mother. A baby is the crown of any woman's achievement.'

'You stupid woman,' Mrs Vickers raged. 'That is only the case if the husband is the father. How long do you think my husband will keep me when he discovers I am pregnant with another man's child?'

So that was it.

Rebecca Vickers realised she had gone too far. She reached for a silver cigarette case, opened it and took out a cigarette. 'Don't seek to advantage yourself with that information,' she said to Paraiti, 'because if you try I'll see you in prison before you can open your mouth.' With delicate fingers she removed a shred of tobacco from her lips, inhaled and then pressed on. 'Are you sure there's nothing that you can do for me?' she asked coolly.

'You are already too far gone,' Paraiti answered. 'You will have to carry the child to term.'

'Have to?' Rebecca Vickers laughed. 'I don't have to do anything.' She exhaled, paused, then said, in a voice that chilled, 'Rip it out of my womb.'

'That would require you to be cut open,' Paraiti said deliberately. Good, the thought of her lovely skin being marked had made Mrs Vickers flinch. 'You would be scarred and carry the evidence of the operation. Your husband would know that something had happened.'

'Men can be so easily duped,' Rebecca Vickers countered. 'And Mr Vickers is an old man who wanted the luxury of a young woman. But he is also a man of class and reputation and . . . he has his vanity. A scar? He would turn a blind eye to that. But evidence that he'd been cuckolded by a younger man? No, his pride would never countenance that. Therefore such an operation wouldn't be too high a price to pay.'

'It is too dangerous. You could die, along with the baby.'

'You've been playing me along.' Rebecca Vickers rose and adjusted her clothes. 'I don't like to be treated as a fool.' Her anger was all the more intense for being so contained. Not a flicker of it disturbed the stillness of her face. 'Maraea will pay you for your consultation. She will give you a cup of tea before you leave.' Her reflection locked gaze with Paraiti, and the room filled with eyes from all the mirrors.

●

Of course it wasn't as easy as that for Paraiti.

The following day, while she was feeding her animals at Waituhi, she saw the local constable, Harry McIntosh, approaching her gate, huffing and puffing. 'What have you done now, eh?' he asked.

She must go with him to Gisborne for questioning. 'Were you in the vicinity of Waterside Drive yesterday? If so, were you invited into the home of Mrs Rebecca Vickers? She has reported that her servant took pity on an old Maori woman who appeared to be faint from the heat, and that her servant gave her something to eat. She left the woman for a moment to talk to the gardener. Now a diamond bracelet is missing.'

Paraiti was taken to the Gisborne jail. For two days she was imprisoned in a cell: a small room, with one square window, a pallet to sleep on and a hole in the ground to crouch over when you wanted to answer Nature's call. There were three other cells containing a scatter of men who watched her curiously as she was locked in; one look at her scar and they turned away.

This was not the first time that Paraiti had been imprisoned. Sometimes, jealous Maori whispered about her clandestine medical activities, which led to arrest and incarceration. On such occasions, Paraiti would think of her parents. 'I am getting off lightly compared with them,' she would say to herself. 'My father was imprisoned for two years, my mother died in jail.'

On the third day, she was dozing when she heard approaching footsteps and someone rapping on the bars of her cell. 'You have a visitor,' Constable McIntosh said.

Dazed from sleep, Paraiti saw that it was Mrs Vickers, her face hidden behind a dark veil, which was sucked in slightly by her breath whenever she spoke. Her eyes were glowing, triumphant. 'So, Paraiti . . . there are more ways than one to skin a cat. I have come to offer you your freedom.'

Behind her, head bowed, was Maraea. 'Please do as she says, takuta,' she pleaded. 'It would be better for all of us.'

'It is dirty, shameful work,' said Paraiti. 'No person would do it.'

'I will pay you handsomely for your work and your silence. If you do what I have already asked of you I will drop the charges.'

'They are false and you know it.'

'Who do you think the authorities would believe?' Rebecca Vickers smiled. 'Someone like me? Or . . .' — her tone was mocking — 'someone like you?'

'Keep your money,' Paraiti said angrily. 'Constable?' she called. 'We've finished our korero here.'

'I will say when our conversation begins and when it ends,' Mrs Vickers hissed between clenched teeth.

Paraiti turned her back to the young woman. 'Get out,' she said.

Rebecca Vickers raised the veil and stepped closer to the bars. 'You doctors,' she continued, 'Pakeha or Maori, you're all the same, kei te mimi ahau ki runga ki a koutou.'

Paraiti gasped, shocked at the precise cultured voice articulating the Maori words. She turned, took a few steps towards Mrs Vickers and peered closely at her.

'Yes, medicine woman, take a good look.' Mrs Vickers turned her head this way and that for the inspection. Paraiti noted again the flawless skin and the cleverly applied make-up. She caught a glimpse of something else: beneath the powder the surface was glazed, as if it had been treated by some whitening agent.

Paraiti took a step back. 'Aue, e hine,' she grieved.

Rebecca Vickers' eyes widened with anger. She had been expecting some other reaction, some acknowledgement of her cleverness. 'What an ignorant woman you are, Scarface.' She smiled mockingly. 'I expected you, at least, to understand.' She lowered her veil and left the cell.

Maraea followed her, but suddenly turned to Paraiti. 'She will kill the baby,' she said, angrily, 'make no mistake about it. If she kills herself in doing it, well — if the baby is born, her life will be destroyed anyhow. Mark my words, you will be as much to blame if you do not help her.'

You doctors, you're all the same, I urinate on all of you.

Paraiti asked the question, even though she already knew the answer. 'He Maori ia?'

'Yes,' Maraea answered. 'She is Maori.'

'But the painting in the house . . . is that not her mother?'

'Yes, it is her mother,' Maraea said.

'Then how . . .'

But Maraea had already gone.

CHAPTER FIVE

I t is another dawn and Paraiti drags her old bones up from
sleep.

She raises her hand in prayer, 'Kororia ki to ingoa tapu,
glory be to Thy holy name,' and praises God again for the gift
of life and the joy of another day. What greater blessing could
humankind receive than to be able to live and breathe, here, on
the bright strand between earth and sky?

Of course, the charge against Paraiti could not be sustained.
Despite Rebecca Vickers' insistence that Paraiti remain in jail,
Harry McIntosh said that an exhaustive search of the two-room
kauta at Waituhi had failed to find the bracelet.

As soon as she was released, Paraiti began her travels.

And now three weeks have passed since Paraiti was in
Ruatahuna.

On her last day there she had presented Horiana with the
bloomers she had bought for her in Gisborne. Horiana had
loved them: 'They're so pretty, it's such a shame to wear them
under my dress! Why don't I wear them on the outside?'

Pulling Kaihe after her and with Tiaki on guard, Paraiti had visited the sick, wounded and elderly of Ruatoki, Waimana and Murupara.

Then, her heart lifting, she set off for Te Kuiti.

●

It was so wonderful for Paraiti to be back among the people who had given sanctuary to her and Te Teira those many years ago. No sooner was she seen entering the village than young children ran up to her, yelling, 'Paraiti! Scarface! You're back!' Even the old chief, Whaturangi, came forward to greet her and tell her to pitch her tent close to Te Tokanganui a Noho, the great Ringatu meeting house.

'Your father would be cross with us if we didn't acknowledge you,' her cousin Peti growled, 'and there are enough angry ghosts floating around us as it is.' Just as Horiana had been Paraiti's assistant in Ruatahuna, so was Peti in Te Kuiti, and she was just as bossy.

Later that evening, in Paraiti's honour, a special remembrance service was held for Te Teira. Sitting in the meeting house, within the latticed walls and with the beautiful painted kowhaiwhai rafters soaring above her, Paraiti again honoured the morehu, the loyal remnants of Te Kooti's followers, survivors in a changing world. And always, she thought of her beloved father and his stories of the prophet Te Kooti.

Te Teira spoke in the words of the Old Testament, likening Te Kooti's exploits to the great exodus and the flight of the Israelites from the lands of Egypt into Canaan. It was all metaphorical talk, but Paraiti was moved by its grandeur and imagery. 'In the end Te Kooti was pardoned,' Te Teira had told her one day. 'I will tell you how. The government wanted to run a railway line through the King Country, and issued a general amnesty to all criminals, no matter what they had done, to secure the land. The prophet was saved by the iron horse!' he laughed.

'It was 1884 when that railway opened,' Te Teira went on. 'You and I were travelling to some Ringatu gathering or other. I can't remember which one, but you were my right-hand man, do you remember? We came across some Maori boys bending over the rails listening. We got off our horses, too, and bent down and listened. And your eyes went big and wide and you said to me, "Papa, the rails are singing a strange waiata!" Then suddenly, around the corner came that iron horse, a huge ngangara, a monster, belching smoke and roaring at us. Our horses started to buck and bolt, but, resolute in the face of the ngangara, you raised your rifle and fired a shot at it.' Te Teira laughed. 'I suppose you were still trying to protect your papa, ne?'

Paraiti's shot did not bring the ngangara to the ground. But as it swayed and slithered past, she saw the many men and women who had been eaten by it, imprisoned in its intestines. She raised a tangi to them, a great lament. Of course, she had been mistaken. The passengers in the train were very much alive — and the ngangara was just another monster eating up the land.

●

It was in Te Kuiti that Paraiti had grown into womanhood. Although Te Teira would have wished for her to marry some kind farmer or fisherman of the tribe, raise children and live a happy life, those choices were closed to her because of her kanohi wera, her burnt face. No matter that he was revered as a tohunga; even his great mana could not obtain a husband for her. She was twenty-four and already habituated to rejection when, in a terrible moment of truth, she asked, 'Papa, what man, in the moment of ecstasy when making love to me, would look upon my face and not wish it was someone else's?' Te Teira himself acknowledged that his daughter was destined to become a spinster, with no provider once he was gone.

But the lives of father and daughter were happy. The only serious threat came when Te Teira had to go underground as legislation was passed against 'charlatan' tohunga. He continued to practise covertly, and he taught his daughter the arts of healing so that she could earn her own living. In particular, he bequeathed to her the rare skill of Maori massage, and the patience to work deep beneath the skin and move muscles and bones and tissue to their proper places, should they be broken, torn or out of alignment.

And when Te Teira was dying of the flu, Paraiti was still massaging him and trying to keep his circulation going long after he became cold.

'Please don't leave me, Father. Please . . .'

●

A stream of patients waited for a consultation, with Peti at the flap of the tent.

A child with chronic asthma will now breathe more easily if he follows the regime of herbal inhalants and exercises that Paraiti has given his anxious parents. The child's young mother had prevailed upon her husband to travel by car from Rotorua on the basis of Paraiti's reputation. 'You took him to the Pakeha doctors and only now you come to see me?' Even so, she grumpily began her diagnosis and, satisfied with it, trickled manuka honey down the child's throat. 'This will soften the mucus.'

She instructed the parents to construct a makeshift sweat tent and fill it with constant steam by boiling water inside the flaps; all the while she continued to trickle the honey — the child sucked on Paraiti's finger as if it was a teat. Oh, to have been a mother!

Three days later, Paraiti put the hook of her little finger down the child's tiny throat and pulled, and strings of softened phlegm came with it. 'Go out into the world now, child,' she blessed him, 'and claim it.'

A young girl was brought in covered in pustules; Paraiti looked after her during the night, using her poultices to draw out the pus and her soporifics to bring down the girl's fever. And if Paraiti was not able to cure all those who sought her help, at least she had tried to make them more comfortable.

One night, Paraiti was woken by the arrival of a cart. In it, lying on blankets, barely conscious, was a man, probably in his early forties. 'Takuta?' he murmured. 'Help!'

Although Maori don't like people arriving in the evening, Paraiti woke Peti so that they could treat the man. 'Bring the light closer,' she said to Peti, who held a Tilley lamp. He was extremely handsome, with curly hair and an open, strong-featured face; he was muscular and tall, with sturdy shoulders.

Two friends had brought him in. 'He has had an accident,' one of them told Paraiti, 'at the mill. We were cutting down a tree and it fell the wrong way and landed on top of him.'

'What is your name?' she asked him.

'Ihaka,' he answered.

When she lifted the blanket she saw that one of his legs was broken in two places. 'You should go to the Pakeha hospital in Hamilton,' she told him.

He moaned and opened his eyes. 'I can't afford it,' he replied. 'Won't you help? I will give you anything.'

'Anything?' Paraiti smiled.

'Well . . .' he said, looking her up and down.

She laughed. 'Think a lot of yourself, don't you!' Then she nodded. 'I will do what they would do,' she told him. 'I will try to save the leg.' No use trying to pretend. 'If I can't, I will have to take it off.'

Ihaka raised himself on his elbows in terror. His face was filled with panic and there were tears of pain in his eyes. 'I need to work, e kui, for my wife and children, and who will employ a one-legged man?' He clutched Paraiti tightly.

At his touch, Paraiti gave a sharp intake of breath: to be touched by him, so strongly, in such an unguarded moment. 'I will do my best,' she said. She had felt . . . his goodness. She gave Ihaka a piece of wood to put into his mouth so that he would not bite his tongue. 'You must be brave, Ihaka,' Paraiti said. 'This is going to hurt, and no amount of herbal painkiller will help you.'

He cupped his genitals; his simple modesty affected Paraiti, and, as she set about the work of resetting his broken bones, she could not help the surge of desire — was it? — that coursed quietly through her. Who would not be affected by such beauty? He began to groan; sweat popped on his forehead.

'Go back to your proper places,' Paraiti said as she began to apply her herbal medicines to his leg and to massage the bones and muscles beneath the skin. Throughout the ordeal, Ihaka tried his best not to cry out, but, when Paraiti started to push and reassemble and manipulate, saying 'Go back! Return, I say!', he gave a loud agonised cry, bit the wood almost in two and became senseless. 'It is better this way,' Paraiti said to his white-faced friends.

All night Paraiti and Peti worked on Ihaka's leg, applying the massage deeper and deeper. Paraiti's fingers sought the fractured bones — three places, yes, three — sensing where she should push them before they would knit and click into place. Over and over she and Peti worked, with immense patience.

'No, don't stop,' she told Peti, when her assistant began to tire.

Finally, however, she was satisfied. 'Prepare the needle and thread,' she said.

Sewing the skin, Paraiti also splinted the leg with palm tree splints and wrapped it with kahakaha bandaging. She sang a song to her needle, telling it to sew sweetly and tenderly and not to scar Ihaka's strong thighs. 'Let his wife look upon him again and not see your pathway,' she sang.

How fortunate that Ihaka was so strong of body, spirit and heart.

And Paraiti poured her great aroha into the young man. Never had she known a man, any man, and so she treated him as the lover she might have had, if she had ever been pretty.

By dawn it was over.

When Ihaka revived, he looked thankfully at Paraiti and kissed her hands. 'You saved my leg?'

She nodded.

'I have no money to pay you,' he said.

'That is all right,' Paraiti answered. 'Let my work be a gift to you. You still have a long road to take before you recover fully. Peti will look after you as you convalesce, giving you the massages I will teach her. May your future be blessed.'

●

With her work over in Te Kuiti, Paraiti said her farewells.

She cut across to the lands of Te Whanau a Apanui: Te Teko and Whakatane. At one point she saw many birds hastening above her head as if escaping some danger, and then she smelt smoke in the air.

'Titiro,' Paraiti said to Kaihe as they reached the top of a mountain ridge. In front of them the entire forest was on fire; Pakeha were clearing the trees to provide more land for the growing river settlement. With an involuntary gesture, Paraiti put a hand to her face as if to protect herself. She wheeled Ataahua and Kaihe away from the blaze, skirting it while embers fell about her. She found a small stream, and, soaking the fabric of her tent, draped it across her horse and mule to protect them from hot ash. Then she slogged on, wrapping a scarf around her face, her eyes watering from the smoke, until she had gained the safety of the lands of Te Karaka.

From there it was only a short ride to Ohiwa, where she rested.

And then it was back to business. More patients, more successful diagnoses and treatments, and always humour, as people laughed in the face of their illness or impending death. Like the old kuia who was wasting away. When Paraiti examined her, she was horrified: 'E kui, you are all skin and bones.' A strong herbal painkiller, and her skilful massaging hands, gave a few more precious days to breathe and to praise the Lord.

Then, just after leaving her clinic at Ohiwa Habour, Paraiti had a disturbing dream. It was a jumble of chaotic images. A face on fire — it was her face. A ngangara bearing down on her; she took up her rifle and shot at it. As the ngangara went by, Paraiti saw a woman with auburn hair coiled within its slithering entrails. What was this? Charlie Chaplin came walking in his familiar way, twirling his cane — how did he get into her dream? He was in a hut and it was see-sawing on the edge of a cliff. But it wasn't Charlie Chaplin at all — it was Paraiti herself. Suddenly, as the hut slid over the cliff, Te Teira appeared, put a hand out and pulled her to safety. Suspended in mid-air, he cupped Paraiti's chin in his hands and wiped her face clear of the scar. He did this again and again. Below, Paraiti saw the hut smash to pieces in the snow.

Paraiti woke up puzzled and anxious. What did the dream mean?

The dream gnawed at Paraiti as she travelled around the coastline from Opotiki to Omaramutu, Torere and Maraenui. Wherever she went, she performed her healing duties. And when she rested, she took Tiaki, Ataahua and Kaihe down to the sea where the horse and mule could soothe their legs in the surf.

Paraiti took Tiaki fishing with her in a favourite lagoon. She speared a fish, but it floated with the spear away from the rocks. 'Kia tere,' she commanded Tiaki. Immediately he dived into the sea after the speared fish, swimming fast and grabbing it just before it sank. 'What would I do without you?' Paraiti winked.

Camping on the beach one evening, Paraiti saw an uncommonly bright star blazing a trail across the sky. That night she had the dream again. It had changed in two respects: the auburn-haired woman had now become the ngangara, and it was a child who was caught in its slithering shape.

●

This morning, Paraiti is waiting for Tiaki to bring her breakfast. Perhaps he has caught a nice silver-finned kahawai.

Of course she will have to throw it back into the sea — first fish to Tangaroa — but the thought of a fish for breakfast is enticing. She leaves her tent to get some driftwood together for a fire to boil water for her manuka tea. She puts a skillet on the flames so it will be ready for Tiaki's catch.

As she is ranging along the beach, with the surf rolling in, she sees an old koroua sitting on a log in the middle of a vast expanse of sand. His trousers are rolled up as if he has just come out of the surf. He is smiling at her and waving to her as if he knows her.

When she sees him, Paraiti's heart bursts with pain and love. She drops her driftwood and runs towards him like a young girl. When she gets nearer, he motions her to sit down next to him.

'Hello, daughter,' Te Teira says. 'Isn't it a lovely morning?'

Paraiti smiles at him. 'Yes, Dad.'

He closes his eyes and sniffs the sea air. 'Mmm, kei te whiti te ra, such a day brings back so many memories, daughter.' He looks at Paraiti again, and she can feel herself drowning in his eyes, irradiated with his love. 'You always had good hands, daughter. They can save lives and they can heal people. You know what you have to do.'

Then he is gone.

After breakfast, Paraiti talks to her animals. 'Well, Tiaki, Ataahua and Kaihe, I know you like to visit kin at Tikitiki, Tokomaru Bay, Tolaga Bay and Whangara, but we have to cancel our travels. Maybe we'll go to Ngati Porou another day. Instead, we are going straight home.'

The animals simply look at her with puzzled expressions. So, what are we waiting for, mistress?

Paraiti puts on her wide-brimmed hat. She packs the saddlebags, says a karakia on the beach and sprinkles sea water over her head and those of her animals. She taps Ataahua on his knees and mounts him.

It will be a long, hard ride. She wants to send a telegram from Opotiki and be at the Waioeka Gorge by nightfall. Although she is reluctant to negotiate the gorge during the day — Pakeha are dynamiting the road where the rock is resistant — she wants to reach Gisborne in two days' time.

Better get a move on.

'Me hoki matou ki te wa kainga,' she orders.

The waves thunder and spray around her as she rides along the beach with her animals and then heads inland.

CHAPTER SIX

Rebecca Vickers waits upstairs in the bedroom of her home on Waterside Drive.

She is smouldering with irritation. Yesterday, Maraea brought news that the Maori medicine woman, Paraiti, had telegraphed from Opotiki to say that she was returning to Gisborne. The message had read: 'We have a matter of mutual benefit to discuss.'

'What are you up to, Scarface?' Rebecca Vickers mutters to herself as she lights a cigarette. 'How presumptuous of you to think you have the upper hand.' Nevertheless, an appointment has been arranged for this evening.

She wears her auburn hair unpinned. She is dressed in a long black robe striped with crimson. Her pregnancy is now clearly showing; her backbone has curved to make space for the baby, and all the other organs have found their places around the whare tangata.

Puffing at the cigarette, she looks out the window. The gardener is working but stops for moment to stretch his back, sees her and quickly goes back to work. 'As well you should,' she says under her breath. 'I will not pay people who shirk their duties.'

The day is already beginning to wane. Rebecca Vickers switches on a reading lamp and rings the bell for Maraea. 'Where's the copy of the *Tatler*? Bring it to me.' When Maraea returns with the magazine, Mrs Vickers stubs out her cigarette and flicks quickly through the pages before pausing at a full-page photograph of Merle Oberon: rich black hair, high noble forehead, exquisite cheekbones, long neck and skin of unsurpassed whiteness. When she was recently in London, Rebecca Vickers had seen the young film actress in her latest role as Anne Boleyn in *The Private Life of Henry VIII*; she had been entranced by that flawless face filling the huge darkness. It is on Merle Oberon's looks, style and manners that she has modelled her own image.

Rebecca Vickers ponders her predicament. Merle Oberon has the world at her feet, but she? In a growing temper she closes the magazine. She is not about to throw away the future for a mere indiscretion, an adulterous affair during her stay in England. But her lover had excited her in a way her elderly husband had never managed to do. Why should she not take some pleasure for herself?

However, it had come to this: an unwanted pregnancy.

Oh, when she had discovered her condition she certainly considered pretending to St John Vickers that the baby was his. She suspected he would have been delighted to have fathered an heir at his advanced age. Indeed, he had been besotted by her ever since he'd met her in Christchurch ten years before. She had been recently widowed — her first husband was Reginald Chichester, a fairly prosperous shipping agent who had died in a dockside accident at Lyttelton. Already passing as white, she had fooled him, too, with her white skin. But Chichester had been a spendthrift, and Rebecca, fallen on hard times, was obliged after his death to work as a hostess at a well-known cabaret frequented by high-spending gentlemen.

St John Vickers, already a notable politician, was entranced by her beauty and sad widowhood and set out to woo her.

As she picks up her hand mirror and looks at her reflection, turning her head this way and that, she catches a hint of darkness in her complexion that a recent application of acid nitrate has not covered.

'Why,' she says, astonished, caressing the blemish, 'there you are, Ripeka.'

She has come a long way from the kainga she left when she was twelve years old. She had never been as dark as her friends, and her features had always been aquiline. In India she would have been called Eurasian, in Latin America mulatto; her beauty would have given her a special status at a quadroon ball in antebellum New Orleans.

But Rebecca Vickers had wanted more than that — she had wanted to cross the colour bar.

As many other women who lacked status and money had done before her, she perfected her masquerade and used her youthful sexuality to rise within Pakeha society. Through two marriages, she gained entry to its most gracious houses, something she would not have obtained by pedigree. And as Mrs Rebecca Vickers, travelling to and from New Zealand, she has finally obliterated all traces of the young Maori girl she once was.

She frowns at the blemish, rubbing it with her left hand so vigorously that the skin reddens. 'No,' she says to her reflection, 'you can never have a child, can you, Ripeka darling, because if you do it may look like you . . .' — she stares into the mirror again — '. . . and not like me.'

The risk is too great.

Suddenly Rebecca Vickers hears footsteps and she sees Maraea appear in the hand mirror.

'Scarface has arrived. She is waiting for you in the living room.'

Paraiti is unprepared for Mrs Vickers' appearance. One month on, pregnancy has given her a transcendent, astonishing beauty. In her black and crimson robe, she looks gorgeous and shimmering, newly emergent in dark shedded skin.

'You said you had a matter of mutual benefit to discuss with me,' Mrs Vickers snaps. 'If you've come to gloat, you can get out now.'

Exhausted from her journey — she has not detoured to Waituhi, and her animals are tied up three streets away — Paraiti takes the upper hand. 'You want something from me,' she says, 'and if you agree to my terms, I will do it. It is too late for an abortion now. But I can begin to bring on the birth of your baby. I can start the procedure tonight if you wish, so that it will come ahead of its time.'

Rebecca Vickers turns her back on Paraiti. To mask her elation she takes a cigarette from a silver case and lights it. Her reflection blazes in all the mirrors in the room. 'Tonight? What is the method?'

'I will give you a compound made from flax, supplejack roots and other herbs that you will drink at least three times a day for the next two weeks. It will bring on contractions and cause your whare tangata to collapse.'

'Is that the extent of the treatment?'

'No, don't assume it will be so easy. The compound will affect the pito, the cord that connects your baby to your womb, and it will begin to constrict. But to hasten the process I will come every second evening to massage the area of the whare tangata so that the baby will not want to stay inside. The massage will be deep, forceful and extremely painful for both of you. If my herbs and the massage have the desired effect, your baby will gladly leave the whare tangata ahead of time.'

'How long will this expulsion take?'

'Fourteen days.'

'Two weeks?' Rebecca Vickers considers the proposal. She rings the bell for the servant, Maraea. 'When does Mr Vickers' ship arrive in Auckland?'

'In twelve days, madam,' Maraea replies.

'He will be expecting me to be waiting for him at the dock...'

Mr Vickers has just been elevated to a ministerial position in the United Party. An anxious prime minister, seeing the way the rival Labour Party is rising in the polls, has called him to return to New Zealand immediately.

Rebecca Vickers turns to Paraiti. 'You must take less time.' It is not a request; it is a command.

Paraiti does not give ground. 'A clever wife like you,' she begins, the sarcasm barely disguised, 'with a loving husband like yours, would easily be able to plead illness as an excuse for not meeting him in Auckland.'

Although Mrs Vickers is defiant she is also vulnerable, and Paraiti's heart goes out to her. 'Why don't you change your mind?' she begins. 'Talk to your husband. He might forgive you.'

The young woman gives an incredulous laugh. 'Forgive me for bearing a child from another man? Yes, he might do that, but forgive me and the child for having a touch of the tar? No, he would never do that.' Her eyes are haunted as she looks at Maraea. 'I might have to go back to the kainga with its dirt, fleas, poverty and . . . harassment.' She holds herself tightly, making brushing movements as if ridding herself of unwanted embraces. 'No, I can never do that.' She looks at Paraiti. 'You, you are so unbeautiful, you would know nothing about the world I left. It was a brutal and angry place for a young mission-educated girl who only wanted to better herself, and because I looked . . . like this . . . men mistreated me in ways that almost broke my valiant spirit. Why aren't you pleased for me that I escaped?'

She stubs out her cigarette.

'Less time, damn you.'

'That is not possible. I have already doubled the number of herbs in the compound. If I increased them again your body might not be able to cope with the strain. You could have a heart attack.'

'You already know how strong I am. Just rid me of my burden.'

'I will not have a dead woman and child on my hands.' She is thinking fast: yes, Mrs Vickers has the stamina. 'You must compromise.'

'You are bargaining with me?' Mrs Vickers laughs, incredulously.

'Fourteen days,' Paraiti answers. 'You do want to live to enjoy the rest of your life, don't you?'

Rebecca Vickers is seething with fury. 'I want to know if the baby will be born dead or alive,' she demands.

Paraiti includes both Mrs Vickers and Maraea in her gaze. 'I can't tell you,' she answers. 'If the baby survives the poisonous and dangerous ordeal as the whare tangata collapses, it will be born alive. If not, I will have to pull it out of you dead.'

Rebecca Vickers has one final question. 'Why are you doing this, Scarface?' She moves with surprising swiftness, cupping Paraiti's chin with one hand and, with the other, stroking the scar that crosses her face. The touch of her hand stings.

'He Maori koe,' Paraiti answers, pulling back. 'You are a Maori.'

'You do this for aroha of me?' Mrs Vickers is probing her soul.

'Kia tupato, tuahine,' Paraiti warns. 'Be careful, Mrs Vickers. You push me and I will change my mind.'

The threat of withdrawal has the desired effect. Rebecca Vickers blinks and steps back, but she is soon on the offensive again. 'You mentioned your terms. What do you want, Scarface? Where is the benefit that you seek for yourself?'

It is now or never. 'I will not require payment for my services,' Paraiti says quickly. 'You will not understand this, Mrs Vickers, but my purpose is to save lives, not take them away. Whether the baby is dead or alive, I will keep it.'

'What are you up to, Scarface? Wait here while I consider.'

Paraiti watches as Mrs Vickers and Maraea leave the room. She hears them talking in low voices. 'I had not realised that your motives would be so selfless,' Rebecca Vickers says on her return, 'but I agree to your request. What choice do I have? You hold all the cards. But I have the easy part of the bargain, not having to dispose of the baby. Are you planning some midnight black magic revel with a dead foetus?' she laughs. 'Do you want to bury it in holy tribal ground? As if that would save its soul?' She is enjoying the way her thoughts are coming to her.

'It's not the baby's soul you should worry about.'

'Enough of this,' Rebecca Vickers says. 'All right, I agree, but twelve days is all I am giving you, takuta, and if by any chance the baby is born alive, take it quickly for I would soon murder it.'

Having asked Maraea to bring up the saddlebag containing her medicines, Paraiti begins the treatment. She instructs both Mrs Vickers and Maraea on the compound and its dosage and frequency. Maraea measures out the first dose and administers it.

Self-confident though she is, Mrs Vickers' eyes show alarm. Her face increases in pallor; after all, it is a poison being administered to her. 'The medicine is making me feel ill,' she says, panicking.

'Be warned,' Paraiti answers, 'it will get much, much worse as we progress.'

She begins the massage. It is light at first and Mrs Vickers relaxes into it. 'This is not so difficult to cope with,' she laughs.

Paraiti goes deeper, stronger, faster — above, around and upon the mound of the whare tangata. Soon, sweat starts to pop out on Mrs Vickers' forehead and she groans, 'No, please, enough, no.' She tries to push Paraiti away.

'Hold your mistress down,' Paraiti says to Maraea.

For half an hour Paraiti keeps up the massage, her eyes dark and her face grim, until Mrs Vickers starts to scream with the pain. Paraiti stops and steps away. Mrs Vickers moans; she can feel the after-effects of Paraiti's manipulations rippling within her womb.

The massage isn't over. Paraiti takes one step forward and, 'Aue! Taukiri e!' she cries as she administers a hard, shocking series of hand manipulations on and around the whare tangata. Then bearing down with both hands she applies relentless pressure on the baby. *Please child, forgive me, but this is the only way.* She can sense the child beneath her hands, fighting the pressure and unbearable pain — and Mrs Vickers screams and loses consciousness.

'Every second day, this?' Maraea asks, horrified.

'Yes,' Paraiti answers. 'Meantime, make sure your mistress drinks the compound. This regime is the only way to achieve what she wants. Under no circumstances can we slow or halt the procedure.'

It is time for Paraiti to leave.

'If Mrs Vickers struggles with me as she has tonight,' she says to Maraea brutally, 'find ropes so that she can be tied down.'

'That won't be necessary.' Mrs Vickers has revived. 'Never will I give you, takuta, that satisfaction.'

'I can find my own way out,' Paraiti answers. She walks to the stairs, but Rebecca Vickers says, 'Wait.'

Paraiti turns to look at her.

'You and I, Scarface, we are not so dissimilar. You wear your scar where people can see it, I wear mine where they can't, but our lives have been affected by them. Me pera taua, we are both the same, you walking unlawfully through your world and I secretly through mine.'

Paraiti pauses a moment longer, then continues down the stairs and along the corridor to the side door. As she leaves, a man steps from the shadows; it is the gardener.

'It was wrong of her, e kui,' he says, 'to put you in jail like that.'

She gives him a grateful glance, then goes down the pathway and closes the gate behind her. She continues along Waterside Drive and, when she is out of sight of the house, her legs fail her and she collapses. 'Oh, child, forgive me for the pain I have done to you tonight.'

My purpose is to save lives, not take them away.

She hears panting and sees that Tiaki has joined her; he licks her face. Sighing to herself, Paraiti joins Ataahua and Kaihe; they could be home by dawn. 'I have gambled tonight,' she says to Tiaki as she mounts Ataahua. 'I have played a game of life and death. Let us pray that I will win.'

Together they fade in and out of the street lights and, finally, into the comforting darkness beyond the town.

CHAPTER SEVEN

Normally, Paraiti would have spent the rest of her haerenga on a circuit of the villages closest to Waituhi. The old woman with a dog, horse and mule are familiar sights among the Ringatu faithful in Turanga, which the Pakeha have renamed Poverty Bay.

She would have journeyed with her travelling garden throughout the lands of Te Whanau a Kai, Te Aitanga a Mahaki, Tai Manuhiri and Rongowhakaata. Wherever the Ringatu festivals took place, wherever the faithful gathered to sing, pray and praise God, there she would be: Waihirere, Puha, Mangatu, Rangatira, Waioeka, Awapuni, Muriwai . . . Still avoiding te rori Pakeha, the Pakeha road, she would instead have ridden the old trails along the foothills or rivers, the unseen pathways that criss-cross the plains like a spider's web.

Instead, for twelve days, Paraiti remains in Waituhi, venturing every second day to Gisborne. When she returns to the village, she goes into Rongopai to pray until dawn. The interior of the meeting house is like a beautiful garden: sometimes, Paraiti has fancifully imagined it as the garden of the Queen of Sheba, where hoopoes sing; at other times it becomes a garden in fabled Babylon, one of many hanging in the palace of Nebuchadnezzar. In this time of agitation and fear, however, Rongopai is like unto the garden of the New Testament at the place called Gethsemane, where a bright, broken Christ was laid to his death and resurrection.

The change in Paraiti's routine worries her neighbours. They look through the doorway of Rongopai at her. She is kneeling before a painting of the tree of life with its healing blossoms. 'Aue, te mamae,' she cries.

'Are you all right, takuta?'

Then others from villages beyond Waituhi come seeking her. 'What is the matter, Blightface?' they ask. 'Are you ill? We need you. What will happen to us?'

Paraiti is patient with them. 'I am only delayed. I will come again soon.'

The concern and enquiries force Paraiti to make an appearance at a Ringatu hui at Takipu, the large meeting house at Te Karaka, so that the people will see she's still alive and kicking. Takipu is so beautiful that Paraiti cannot help but be grateful that her whakapapa connects her to such a glorious Ringatu world.

The hui incorporates a kohatu ceremony, an unveiling of the headstone of a brother Ringatu healer, Paora, who died a year ago. The obelisk, the final token of aroha, is polished granite, gleaming in the sun. It is a sign of the love for a rangatira. As Paraiti joins the local iwi, weeping, around the obelisk, she reflects on the fragility of life. 'Not many of us morehu left,' she thinks to herself. Afterwards, she spends some time talking to Paora's widow, Maioha: 'It was a beautiful unveiling for a man who always served God and the people.'

'Ae,' Maioha says. 'However, we must go on, eh? The men

may be the leaders, but when they die, it is the women who become the guardians of the land and the future.'

On the way back to Waituhi, Paraiti cannot shake off Maioha's words. Her mood deepens as she thinks of all the changes she has observed in her travels. Since she and her father saw the ngangara those many years ago — the train steaming across the countryside — the marks of the new civilisation have proliferated across the land. New railway tracks, highways and roads. More bush felled to make way for sheep and cattle farms. Where once there was a swing bridge there is now a two-lane bridge across the river. And although the old Maori tracks are still there, many of them have barbed-wire fences across them, necessitating a detour until a gate is found. On the gate is always a padlock and a sign that says: 'Private Land. Trespassers will be prosecuted. Keep out.'

The changes are always noted by the travellers of the tracks and passed on to other travellers — 'Kia tupato, beware' — because, sometimes, horses or children can be ensnared in the coils of barbed wire discarded in the bush after the fences have been built. Paraiti has sewn up many wounds inflicted by the wire as pig hunters and foresters have rushed after prey in the half-light of dusk.

But of all the changes wreaked by civilisation, it is the spiritual changes that really matter. The ngangara is not only physical; it also infiltrates and invades the moral world that Paraiti has always tried to protect.

You wear your scar where people can see it, I wear mine where they can't.

Perhaps the marks that really matter are, indeed, the ones that can't be seen.

●

The twilight is falling as Paraiti returns to Waituhi from Te Karaka.

Tiaki pricks up his ears and sniffs ahead. He begins to growl.

'He aha?' Paraiti enquires. 'What is it?'

She sees that smoke is coming out of the chimney of her two-roomed kauta. When she gets to the gate, a horse is grazing in the front paddock. She reaches into her saddlebag for her rifle and commands Tiaki to be alert. Then she hears someone chopping wood at the back of the house.

'That's not the sound of danger,' she says to herself.

A man, stripped to the waist, his trousers held up by braces, is balancing on crutches, chopping wood. The falling light limns him with gold. Who can it be?

Paraiti realises it is the logger from Te Kuiti whose leg had been broken. At the sight of him Tiaki begins to growl: he is jealous and doesn't like any other male company around his mistress.

'Turituri,' Paraiti scolds him. She watches Ihaka, amused. 'So what's a man on crutches doing chopping wood in my back yard?' she asks.

He puts the axe down and grins at her. 'Paying my debt to you,' he answers. 'I have heated water for a bath and the fire is on in the kauta to make it warm.'

A bath? Paraiti's eyes light up. 'You didn't have to do that.'

'I won't take long filling the tub,' Ihaka responds and then — oh, he's a cheeky one — 'Don't worry, I'm not going to look as you get into it.'

It's dark by the time Paraiti gets out of the bath. When she enters the big room of the kauta, Ihaka has washed and put on a clean shirt.

And he has set the wooden table with a plate of damper

bread and pots of puwha, potatoes and bacon bones. 'I brought these with me,' he says. 'They won't last, so we may as well eat them. Would you like me to say a karakia for our food?'

Paraiti nods her head, perplexed. What is happening?

After grace, Ihaka dishes out the food. He is courteous and polite, attentive to her every need. 'Would you like more bacon bones? I picked the puwha from your own vegetable garden. I hope you don't mind — I'll replace the plants if you do. Let me get you some more damper bread. Would you like some water to wash the meal down?'

The meal completed, Paraiti thanks Ihaka. 'You are a good cook, and I have not had anybody make kai for me for a long time.'

The room is warm from the fire, and the oil lamp casts a golden glow through the interior. Paraiti's heart is beating fast. Tiaki does not like the situation at all; his ears are flattened on his head and he keeps showing his teeth.

And then Ihaka coughs, gets up, eases Paraiti from her chair and gently pulls her into a hongi, a pressing of noses. She tries to break away from him but he is so strong, his breath so sweet. To soothe her, he begins to kiss her scar.

'No.' Paraiti pushes him away.

'I have a debt to pay,' he answers. 'I am a man of honour. Let me repay it.'

How? Not like this. 'You are much younger than I am, and you have a wife and children.'

'A woman must have a good man at least once in her life,' Ihaka says.

Paraiti has always been alone with her animals, unloved by any man except her father. She can't help it: tears flood from her eyes. 'Yes,' she nods, 'and I know you are a good man.'

It takes quite a while for Paraiti to recover. Only when Tiaki noses himself into her does she stop weeping. 'Thank you,

Ihaka,' she says, blowing her nose, 'but . . .' — she gestures at Tiaki — '. . . as you can see, you have a rival.' She takes a deep breath and, in releasing it, lets Ihaka go. 'Nor would Tane, God of the Forest, like it if I did not offer the first fruit — you — back to him.'

'Are you sure?'

'I am sure,' she smiles, pressing his hands with hers. 'Go back to your wife. And you don't have to look so relieved!'

'She knows I am here. Because of you I am still a good provider, and my wife . . . she knows I am pleasing to look at. She told me, "Let your beauty be our gift to the takuta."'

'Your wife said that? Thank her for her generosity.'

Quickly, before she changes her mind, Paraiti shows Ihaka to the door.

'Goodnight, takuta,' he says.

For a long time afterwards Paraiti wanders around the kauta. Ihaka's scent is everywhere. Tiaki doesn't like it, endeavouring to urinate in a corner.

Paraiti starts to giggle. 'Don't do that,' she scolds.

Then she opens all the windows and doors.

Breathes in deeply.

Turns her thoughts to tomorrow.

CHAPTER EIGHT

The star cluster of Matariki has burst into its fullness in the night sky.

How Paraiti manages to get through the second week, she will never know. She prays constantly, morning, noon and night, her karakia unceasing and seamless. All that sustains her as she hastens to Waterside Drive every second day is her immense faith, and the words of her father: 'You know what you have to do.'

But every time Maraea meets her at the side door, saying 'Come in, quickly, before you are seen', Paraiti feels sick to her stomach that all her efforts might be for nought — that, instead of saving the baby, she will be complicit in its death. Indeed, as she steps through the doorway she finds comfort in knowing that the Ringatu gardener is watching — somewhere he is out there, going about his work, pretending not to know what is happening inside.

It doesn't matter if he sees, for he is only a worker; but it does matter if others do, the high-class neighbours, the leaders of Gisborne society, for they are the ones who hold the power.

And so Paraiti continues the regime. First, the administering of the lethal compound designed to shrivel the birth cord and expel the baby from the womb. Second, the deep, forceful, disturbing massage: out, out, come out. She brings Rebecca Vickers from groaning to screaming point, and then those rapid hand manipulations followed by the pressure exerted on the womb.

Paraiti realises, however, her anxiety must be as nothing when compared with that of the baby in the womb. What must it be like to be in the house of birth, a whare meant to nurture and sustain, as its walls and roof are caving in, as the stitched tukutuku are ripping apart, the kowhaiwhai panels are cracking? Where can the baby go when the poutokomanawa begins to collapse and the poisons begin to flood through the placenta that feeds it? Even when it is fighting back, how can it know that even this is anticipated and is part of its brutal eviction?

As she pummels, she imagines the child trying to retreat into the recess of the womb looking out, as if through a doorway to a world collapsing all around it, facing the terror of the unknowable, its little heart beating hard against translucent skin. *What is happening? Help me.*

'Forgive me, child, oh forgive me,' she whispers.

Ironically, Rebecca Vickers' own strength is working in the baby's favour for, whether she likes it or not, her baby has inherited her stamina.

And so child fights mother: I will not let you do this. Indeed, for Paraiti, the long moments after each savage treatment are always frightening. Will the baby rally? Will her heartbeat come back?

Child, fight. Fight.

Meanwhile, Mrs Vickers has bought herself the last two

days. Her vanity has persuaded her that after the premature birth she would like time to recover and present herself to her husband as immaculately as she can. She has sent him a telegram on board his ship, to say that she will be unable to meet him in Auckland. A reply has come: although he is disappointed, he will spend the evening in the city before travelling on to Gisborne.

Thus, on the twelfth day, when Mrs Vickers groans, 'Now, Scarface, do your work and rid me of this child', Paraiti takes the advantage presented to her.

'The door of the whare tangata is not wide enough to enable the baby's delivery.'

Turning a deaf ear to Mrs Vickers' torrent of curses, Paraiti tells her, 'I will do it on the morning of the fourteenth day, before sunrise.' Every hour will improve the baby's chance of survival.

'Mr Vickers will be home that evening,' Mrs Vickers cries.

'Lock your door. Tell him you are still indisposed.'

Mrs Vickers' rage pursues Paraiti into the street, but the medicine woman is beyond caring about her. Her thoughts are only with the child. 'Kororia ki to ingoa tapu,' she prays to the evening sky and all throughout the next day. Her animals, sensing her anxiety, honour her fervency with barks, whinnies and brays of their own; otherwise, they stand and wait in silence and on good behaviour.

●

Now has come the fourteenth day, before sunrise.

Paraiti arrives at the side door, where she is admitted by Maraea. Rebecca Vickers waits in her bedroom. 'You think you have trumped me,' she snarls. 'Well, two can play at that game, Scarface.'

The final treatment has forced her waters to break. The birth has begun. The contractions are coming strongly — and the baby has slipped from the whare tangata into the birth canal.

Paraiti ignores the threat. 'Your trial will soon be over,' she answers, 'and it will be advisable for you to focus on the difficulties ahead. A normal birth is difficult enough. One that has been induced as forcefully as this is more so.'

Yes, Rebecca Vickers has stamina all right but, even so, she is being truly tested. She is dressed in a white slip, the cloth already stained at her thighs. Her skin shines with a film of sweat.

'You wish to be delivered of the baby here?' Paraiti asks.

'Here, fool?' Mrs Vickers asks. 'In my matrimonial bed where I would be reminded of the birth of an illegitimate child every time I sleep in this room?' She motions to Maraea to help her up.

'How do you wish to give birth, Mrs Vickers?' Paraiti asks. 'The Maori way or the Pakeha way?' She knows the question has a hint of insolence about it, but, after all, Mrs Vickers has Maori ancestry and it needs to be asked. The Pakeha position is prone, unnatural; even so, Paraiti assumes that this is the way Mrs Vickers would wish the baby to be delivered.

Her answer, however, surprises Paraiti. 'My mother has prepared a place so that I can deliver the Maori way,' she says. 'What does it matter? The child will be born dead anyway.'

It is a slip of the tongue, accidental. However, her next words are not.

'If it was good enough for my mother's child,' she says, looking at Maraea, 'it is good enough for mine.'

●

Maraea? Mrs Vickers' mother?

'You stupid girl,' Maraea says, looking at Paraiti.

'Oh, what does it matter if Scarface knows,' Mrs Vickers answers. 'She is of no consequence.'

Who holds the upper hand here? All this time Paraiti had thought that Mrs Vickers was the dominant one. 'Ko koe te mama?' she asks Maraea, and she looks at the older woman to affirm the relationship.

Maraea holds her gaze. She nods briefly. 'Yes, I am Ripeka's mother. And it would be best if you held this knowledge to yourself . . .'

'Or what?' Within the words is an implied threat.

Maraea retreats, puts on the garb of subservience. 'I never thought the pathway would lead to this, Scarface, believe me.' There is no resemblance at all. One is old, dark, seemingly indecisive; the other young, fair, purposeful. Or is the old one as passive as she would lead you to believe? What kind of unholy relationship, what kind of charade, is this between daughter and mother?

Paraiti refuses to let Maraea get away that easily. 'You call yourself a Maori. You are nothing.'

Maraea rears at her. 'Don't you judge me, Scarface. You live safely among your own; you try to survive in a world that is not your own. I have done what every mother, Maori or not, would do: give my daughter every chance at success. Her success is my success.'

Clearly, the painting on the landing is a lie. It is not Rebecca's mother at all, but simply a ruse to put people off the scent.

Rebecca Vickers gives a guttural moan. 'Take me to the birthing place. Quickly.'

Leading the way, and supporting her daughter as she goes, Maraea beckons Paraiti down the stairs to the ground floor of the house. Through the kitchen they go to a set of doors leading to an underground basement. There's a circular staircase and then a further set of steps to a small cellar.

'This is the place,' Maraea says, switching on a light. The cellar is a large hole cut out of the dark, wet clay, barely high enough to stand up in. It is where Mr Vickers stores his vintage wine.

Paraiti sees that Maraea has done her work well. Two hand posts have been dug into the clay, and beneath the place where Mrs Vickers will squat are clean cotton blankets and a large sheet to wrap the baby in.

With a cry of relief, Rebecca Vickers shrugs off her slip and, naked, takes her place between the posts in a squatting position, thighs apart. Her pendulous breasts are already leaking milk. 'No, I won't need those,' she says to Maraea, refusing the thongs that her mother wants to bind her hands with. 'Do your work, Scarface,' she pants, 'and make it quick.'

Maraea has already taken a position behind her, supporting her.

'Massage your daughter,' Paraiti commands. 'Press hard on her lower abdomen and whare tangata so that the baby is prompted to move further downward.'

The whare tangata is collapsing. But there is a heartbeat — faint, but a sign that the baby has survived the rigours of the internal punishment.

'I am here, child,' Paraiti whispers. 'Kia tere, come quickly now.' She takes her own position, facing Rebecca Vickers, and presses her knees against her chest. In this supreme moment of childbirth, the young woman is truly transformed: Mother Incarnate, her red hair is plastered to her skull, sweat is beading her forehead and her entire body streams with body fluids. She is magnificent.

'You will pay for this,' she says. Suddenly her face is in

rictus. She takes a deep breath, her mouth opens in surprise and her groan seems to echo down to the very moment of the creation of the world. She is one mother, but she is all mothers.

Paraiti places her hands on Mrs Vickers' swollen belly. Oh, the baby is too slow, too slow, so she must administer a series of sharp, forceful blows — one, two, three, *four* — to give it the impetus to kick itself outward with its last remaining strength.

The baby pushes head first against the birth opening.

Paraiti's manipulation is firm and vigorous. The contractions are rippling stronger and stronger, and the fluids stream from the vagina as the doorway proudly begins to open. 'Now, bear down,' Paraiti orders.

Mrs Vickers does not flail the air. Her face constricts and she arches her neck with a hiss. With a gush of blood, undulation after undulation, the baby slides out, head followed by shoulders, body and limbs, into the world. The baby is dark-skinned with wet, matted red hair.

'A girl,' Paraiti whispers in awe. 'Haere mai, e hine, ki Te Ao o Tane. Welcome, child, to the world of humankind.' Quickly, she cradles the child, wiping the mucus from her face to give her the first breath of life from one generation to the other.

She feels Maraea's fingers digging into her, pulling her back. 'No, let it die.'

Paraiti pushes her away. Alarmed, she notices that the baby is very still. She clears the baby's mouth and massages her chest.

Still no movement.

Maraea is on her with a growl, but Paraiti pushes her away again. She breathes through the child's nose and mouth and then gives the *ha*, the blessing through the fontanelle.

The baby cries. Her eyes open. They are green, shining, angry.

'Oh,' Mrs Vickers whispers.

Rebecca Vickers motions for Paraiti to give the baby to her.

When Paraiti looks at her, she realises Mrs Vickers has been surprised into love.

'Look, Mother,' she says to Maraea.

Paraiti has brought with her a sharp cutting shell to sever the umbilical cord. 'Hui e, haumi e, taiki e,' she whispers. 'Let it be done.'

She ties the cord with flax. She closes her eyes, feeling suddenly tired. When she opens them, she sees that Mrs Vickers is weeping. Where is the child?

'My mother has taken it. It had no future anyway.'

●

All along Paraiti should have realised.

When Maraea had said, on their second meeting, 'She will kill the baby, make no mistake about it', what she had really meant was that she, the mother and not the daughter, would kill it. The baby's birth threatened not only Rebecca's life but Maraea's too, and she wasn't about to let it be destroyed.

Paraiti rushes up from the basement. Behind her, she hears Mrs Vickers calling, 'My mother will not kill the baby in this house. She wants to, but she knows of the spiritual consequences of such an act — of having a child ghost destroy the calmness of her life. But she will get rid of it.'

Through the kitchen Paraiti runs. The back door is open and she hears the distant crunch of Maraea's feet on the gravel path. The front gate makes a slight sound as it opens and shuts. Across the garden, the light snaps on in the gardener's house and he comes to the doorway, silhouetted in the light.

'E Tiaki,' Paraiti calls to her dog, 'kia tere. Follow.'

Keeping to the shadows, Tiaki slinks silently in pursuit.

Paraiti follows, watching for a glimpse of Maraea as she flees beneath the moon.

'She's heading for the bridge,' Paraiti says to herself, alarmed. On the other side is a small Maori settlement.

Paraiti hears a thin wail from the baby. She cannot believe that Maraea intends to throw the child into the river.

But she does, as if she is throwing a sack of kittens.

'Aue, e hine,' Paraiti cries.

Paraiti could go quickly to the rescue but some inner sense tells her: *Wait. Don't let Maraea know you are in the darkness.* Indeed, not long afterwards, Maraea can be heard returning to Waterside Drive.

Once she has gone, Paraiti runs to the bridge to look over. Good fortune has attended the child. The sack has air in it, giving it buoyancy. It is floating away on the dark river; it won't be too long before it sinks.

'Haere atu,' Paraiti yells to Tiaki. She points at the sack in the river and he jumps off the bridge and splashes into the water.

Paraiti's heart is beating fast as she slips and slides down to the river's edge. She can hear the thin wail of the child again. 'Kia tere, kia tere!' she urges Tiaki. The sack is becoming waterlogged and it is sinking. 'Quick, Tiaki, quick.'

He is too late. The sack disappears under the water.

With a yelp, Tiaki dives for it — has not his mistress taught him at a favoured lagoon to bring back speared fish from the sea? But the sack has already gone too deep, too deep. Then something flicks across his nose, a piece of twine trailing from the sack as it sinks deeper, and he lunges . . .

Tiaki breaks out of the water. In his teeth, he has the sack. 'He kuri pai!' Paraiti calls to him. 'Good dog. Whakahokia mai te kete ki ahau.' But the sack, waterlogged, is too heavy and is dragging Tiaki down with it. 'Tiaki,' Paraiti cries, 'have strength, kia kaha.'

Then comes the sound of someone running past her and diving into the water. It is the Maori gardener. With swift strokes he makes midstream and dives. When he surfaces, he has the sack. 'Bring it to me,' Paraiti urges. 'Quickly.'

The gardener thrusts the sack into Paraiti's hands. Her usually clever fingers are so clumsy! They take so long to untie the knot. 'Do your work quickly, fingers, quickly.'

The baby is so still, with a tinge of blue on her skin. She already has the waxen sheen of death upon her.

'Move quickly, hands. You have always healed, always saved lives. Give warmth to the child, massage the small heart and body to beat again and to bring the water up from her lungs. Quickly, hands, quickly. And now—'

The gardener is in despair — 'The baby is already gone' — but Paraiti will not give up. She holds the child and gives her three sharp taps on her chest. 'If you breathe, I promise you that this will be the last time I hit you.'

And the heart begins to pump and the baby yells, spraying water out of her mouth. She starts to cough; that's good, as she will get rid of all the water from her lungs. Very soon she is breathing and crying, and Paraiti continues to rub her down, increasing her body warmth.

Tiaki noses in to see what she is doing. He whimpers and licks her. 'Oh, pae kare,' the gardener says to himself, 'Oh, thank God.'

Paraiti takes a moment to calm down. 'Thank you,' she says to the gardener. Then she addresses the baby. 'I will call you Waiputa,' she says. 'Born of water.'

She sprinkles her head with water to bless her. Waiputa is already nuzzling Paraiti's breasts.

'You're not going to have any luck with those old dugs,'

Paraiti tells her. 'I'd better find you a wet nurse.' She looks across the river at the Maori settlement; there's bound to be some younger woman there, breastfeeding her own child, who owes Paraiti a favour and won't mind suckling another infant.

As for the future? Paraiti smiles to herself. 'What a menagerie we will make, Waiputa! A scar-faced woman, two old nags, a pig dog and you.'

Others had begun their lives with less.

CHAPTER NINE

Seven years later, time has been kind to Paraiti. Although her eyesight has dimmed a little, her memory is as sharp as ever, her medical skills intact, and her hands still do their blessed work. Tiaki has grown a bit greyer and is not as formidable a hunter as he used to be. Both Ataahua and Kaihe are casting a keen eye on the pasture across the road where they can live out the rest of their years.

This morning Paraiti woke as usual at dawn, said her karakia, performed her ablutions, packed her saddlebags and set off down the road. She still makes her annual haerenga and, in the year 1942, she is on her way to a hui at Te Mana o Turanga, Whakato marae, Manutuke, the birthplace of the prophet Te Kooti. Oh, how she loves that meeting house. So full of carvings and stories of the people. Whenever she visits, it is as if the past comes to life before her.

She is looking forward to the hui, too, the celebration of the Passover on November the first, when what has been planted at Matariki is harvested — symbolic of the resurrection of Christ. A special karakia is also planned: with a European war happening on the other side of the world, and Maori soldiers fighting in Italy, Paraiti will join others in praying that the Angel of Death will pass over them without reaping his harvest.

●

Paraiti usually travels by the side of the Pakeha roads now. Many of the great Maori trails are fenced off, and the last time she travelled on Rua's Track, she had trouble hanging on when she was negotiating the steepest part. But she still grumbles about the ways that civilisation is advancing through the world, and she is always pointing out more of its marks.

She comes to the fork of the road where roadmen have been constructing a combined road-and-rail bridge. She's never seen one quite like it. The road has been made of a black and sticky material. Tiaki sniffs at it and growls. Ataahua and Kaihe stand patiently waiting for the order to move across.

'It might be like the Red Sea,' Paraiti mutters. 'We could be halfway across and next minute, aue, the waves will come over us.'

'No it won't, Nan,' a young voice says. 'It's called tar seal. Come on, there's no traffic. Let's cross now.'

Riding Kaihe is a pretty young girl, fair, with auburn hair. Paraiti has an assistant now, a whangai daughter, Waiputa, to fill her waning years. She is someone to love; the new seed for the future, blossoming from Paraiti's old life. In turn, Waiputa is someone who loves her matua, her parent.

They make a good team, the scarred one and the unscarred one.

'Tar seal, eh?' Paraiti answers. 'You're learning lots of big words at that school of yours.'

Not only that, but Waiputa has become a very firm dealer in the transactions whenever Paraiti heals someone; Waiputa makes sure her nan is not shortchanged.

Paraiti pulls Kaihe across the black river. Aue, motorised traffic is faster than an old woman with her horse, mule and pig dog, and a little girl riding the mule. It can come out of nowhere and is onto you before you know it. Now, roaring across the bridge like a ngangara, comes a huge sheep truck and trailer.

'Quickly, Nan,' Waiputa says. 'We have to get to the other side of the road or we'll be run over.'

Paraiti knows how fast she can go. Quick? She is already at quick. There's nothing to do except face the ngangara.

'E tu,' she says to Ataahua and Kaihe. Together, they turn to the oncoming monster. Paraiti reaches for her rifle.

The truck driver signals to her to get off the road and then, alarmed, sees that she has raised a gun and is sighting it. He slams on the brakes: 'Shit!'

The truck squeals to a halt, its trailer rattling, wheezing, collapsing before the old woman and her whangai daughter. The driver swears and starts to open the door to give the kuia a piece of his mind. When he sees the old, greying dog snarling and the little red-haired girl baring her teeth, he shuts it again, rapidly. 'Stupid old woman,' he yells at Paraiti as she goes past him. He waits until she has crossed the road before starting his truck and proceeding on his way.

Waiputa watches the truck disappearing down the road. She wags a finger at Paraiti. 'Bad girl, Nan. We could have been killed.'

'I know,' Paraiti answers. 'And I realise it was just a truck. But you know, in the old days, I would have shot it.'

Paraiti peers at the sun and begins to laugh and laugh. Then, looking at the road ahead, she pulls down her hat and says to Waiputa, Tiaki, Ataahua and Kaihe:

'Looks like we're just going to have to last forever.'

WHITE LIES
THE
SCREENPLAY

DANA ROTBERG

FROM THE NOVELLA MEDICINE WOMAN TO THE FILM WHITE LIES – TUAKIRI HUNA SCRIPTWRITER AND DIRECTOR'S NOTES

When I first read *Medicine Woman* by Witi Ihimaera, in the collection *Ask the Posts of the House* (Reed Books, 2007), I found it a perfect piece of storytelling. A balanced structure that contained complexity, was generous in its understanding of human drama and had a delightful sense of humour. A profound story but not a pretentious one. A little gem! The story would not leave my mind. It kept visiting me while I was driving on the motorway, when falling asleep, while cooking... Paraiti, the medicine woman, was a stubborn presence who refused to leave and I became haunted by her.

I felt that was a clear sign that the story told by Witi Ihimaera was speaking to me from places other than where the original work had come from. Places that belonged to my intimate family history and my most unresolved conflicts as a person in the world. It was a call from the core of my origins to look for answers that mattered to me, being myself a half-caste, a woman, a mother and a descendant of people who have been eternal immigrants or brutally colonised by others. A call coming from every drop of the Mexican, Jewish, Catholic, Polish, indigenous, Italian, Spanish and Russian blood that runs through my veins. The blood of my tipuna. My very own whakapapa.

Never uprooted from its origins, but with enough independence to become an organic entity with a purpose of its own, the creative process of writing an adaptation and imagining a film story is the work of an alchemist. For that process to happen, I asked Witi Ihimaera if he would give me freedom and independence from him as an author, and allow me to take the original novella *Medicine Woman* and transform it first into a screenplay and ultimately a film: *White Lies — Tuakiri Huna*. Witi was generous and trusted me. Only then could this script have been conceived and a film born.

Writing the script *White Lies — Tuakiri Huna* has been for me an uninterrupted experience of adaptation, not only through the process of transforming a literary work into a cinematographic expression, but also as a pilgrimage through a cultural, linguistic and spiritual vision that was unknown to me.

I was privileged to be guided by people who know the Maori culture from deep within. People who honour the tikanga and who are proud guardians of a sacred knowledge.

THE SCREENPLAY AND THE FILM

ADAPTATION

1. the act or process of adapting.

2. adjustment to environmental conditions, as:
   A. adjustment of a sense organ to the intensity or quality of stimulation
   B. modification of an organism or its parts that makes it more fit for existence under conditions of its environment.

3. something that is adapted; *specifically*: a composition rewritten into a new form.
   — MERRIAM-WEBSTER ONLINE DICTIONARY

Adapting an original work of literature into a film makes sense to me only when the story can be filtered through my own identity as a filmmaker and as a human being. The heart of literature and cinema each palpitate with a different beat. They have different needs in terms of the narrative devices, skills and tools required for a story to be told.

Looking for answers to the demands of the specific language of cinema, I made fundamental changes in the transition from the novella *Medicine Woman* to the screenplay. These changes took the story of Paraiti, Rebecca and Maraea to a new destination: the film *White Lies — Tuakiri Huna*.

THE TITLE: LIES THAT KILL

'Verdades a medias; mentiras que matan'

There is a popular saying in Mexico: *'Verdades a medias: mentiras que matan'*. In English it would be something like: 'Half-truths are lies that kill'. I looked for an equivalent to that saying in English, and I believe *White Lies* is the right expression within the setting of the film. In the historical context of colonisation it conveys precisely the meaning of that piece of Mexican popular wisdom. While normally the saying 'white lies' refers to 'lies told to avoid hurting someone', in the film the term has a double meaning: the traditional meaning and a literal one. When the literal and the traditional collide, the title becomes a more complex phrase, reflecting the layers of deceit and suffering being explored in the story. Ani Prip, Hineira Woodward and Mina Prip, who knew the script from its earliest origins, gifted us with the te reo Maori translation of *Tuakiri Huna**.

That is the origin of the title of the film, born from the novella *Medicine Woman*. All through the voyage of languages and cultures, the fundamental concepts of the original work, written by Witi Ihimaera, have been retained. I believe that this is the most precise example of how the human conflict of identity and truth is a universal drama, no matter in which language, era or culture it is seeded.

---

*Tuakiri Huna: Tua: Beyond, on the other side of. Kiri: skin. Tuakiri, which combines both words, becomes: Identity, personality. Huna: To conceal or hide.
SOURCE: ANI PRIP

THE CONTEXT: A MYTHIC PIECE OF TUHOE HISTORY AND A FABLE ABOUT HOPE

In the culture in which I was raised, mythology was either the exclusive territory of a remote god of unappeasable nature, with an indifferent and imperative will, or the playground where capricious and moody gods imposed their complicated ways onto the destiny of human pawns.

In Maori cosmology, the origin of myth is rooted in and nurtured by the legacy of the ancestors. The deeds and misfortunes of the tipuna can be traced through each person's whakapapa, paving the route back to their most primal narrative and essential traditions. It is in the living memory of the people that history and mythology breathe from the same source. And it is from there, as well, that the everyday reference to right and wrong takes place, and where the fibres that weave the tikanga are harvested. Origin, mythology and identity are not just a reflection of Maori ways and reasons of being — they are one and the same, always inextricably intermingled, like an ancient heart flooding blood to the present. The scale and dynamics of all this fascinate me.

The myths of people cannot happen away from their land — they are interconnected. The story of the film *White Lies* — *Tuakiri Huna* has its natural origin in Te Urewera, as it is there, in the land of the Tuhoe people, that Witi Ihimaera placed Paraiti the medicine woman — it could be no other way.

The Tuhoe story 'Te Tatau Pounamu' was a major source of inspiration to me during the process of writing this script.

'Te Tatau Pounamu' (the greenstone door of peace)

By the early 1830s, Tuhoe were equipped. They became involved in extensive attacks on other tribal groups in the central North Island. It is from the

*fighting in these years that a seminal oral narrative
of Tuhoe, which would be reworked over time,
emerges: the story of Paora Kiingi I (Paora Te Au or
Te Tawai), who chose to halt the fighting.*

*A senior grandson of Te Unuaraki, Paora Kiingi I
assembled a vast military expedition intended
to avenge his grandfather's death in battle at
Whangara, on the East Coast. The Mataatua waka
tribes co-operated in building a large canoe out
of a totara felled in the Huiarau ranges, but it did
not leave the mouth of the Whakatane River. At the
feast held just before their planned departure in
1829, Paora Kingii I aborted the expedition. Instead,
accompanied by his uncle, Te Whenuanui I, he
journeyed to the East Coast to create 'te tatau
pounamu' (the greenstone door of peace), a binding
covenant.*

Encircled Lands, Te Urewera, 1820–1921, *Judith
Binney (Bridget Williams Books, 2009)*

In the film, Paraiti journeys from the initial belief that victory
is only accomplished through an act of revenge, to the eventual
discovery that no one ever wins unless it is through the
resolution of 'te tatau pounamu', the covenant of peace — no
matter the name of the enemy, or the colour of their skin. This
is an element that deepens Paraiti's connection to the identity
and history of the Tuhoe, and at the same time gives her the
universality of someone who honours humanity and whose
heart is capable of compassion beyond race.

I feel privileged and honoured for the opportunity I had in
this film to rework this piece of Tuhoe history.

THE STORY: ABOUT
COLONIALISM AND IDENTITY

Faced with the imposition of a foreign cosmogony — as the colonial phenomenon is, no matter in which part of the world or when in history it happens — there are two separate questions that hold the key to survival:

Who are we?

Where do we belong?

The research of this theme was the main motivation that guided me through the process of writing the script. This is what the film *White Lies — Tuakiri Huna* is all about.

Tradition or assimilation? Tolerance or denial? Life or death? Utu or a covenant of peace?

To place such questions and find the answers, I changed the inner motivation of the characters and the dramatic dynamics between them. The intention behind this narrative structure is to provide each one of the characters in the film with the role of expressing and embodying their search. Paraiti, Rebecca Vickers, Maraea and the unborn baby are shaped in the film to give voice and meaning to the very core of the discovery and creation of their true identities. The dramatic element that ignites and fuels the narrative of this film is the experience of motherhood, the primal and universal symbol of identity, continuity and life.

In the film, Paraiti, Rebecca Vickers and Maraea — our three main characters — are bonded by a pregnancy that each one of them faces from different and opposing perspectives. An unborn child, the very symbol of hope and the future, becomes a main character in the story, imposing on each one of these women inescapable confrontations. The challenges and choices that Paraiti, Rebecca Vickers and Maraea face will finally guide each to find out who they are and where they belong, even when such a discovery points to a tragic destiny.

The journey of these women is not only a symbol of how the fabric of contemporary New Zealand was woven, but also a fable of hope in a world still not aware of the very simple truth that the choice of creation over destruction, tolerance instead of suppression, is the only possible way.

THE DYNAMICS BETWEEN CHARACTERS: TUAKIRI HUNA, A DANCE OF HIDDEN IDENTITIES

In the novella *Medicine Woman*, Witi Ihimaera holds the dramatic action through a narrative structure of two parallel forces — Paraiti and Rebecca Vickers. Maraea, in the novella, retains her Maori identity but is basically a passive element as the silent servant obedient to the wishes of her daughter and mistress.

In the screenplay and later on in the film, Maraea goes through a radical transformation. She becomes the most active element in the drama; she is the unseen designer and doer of all, the puppet master behind all actions. It is Maraea who imposes on Rebecca Vickers the bleaching of her skin, kidnapping the true Maori identity from her daughter.

Rebecca Vickers, then, is the result of her mother's wishes. She is, in the film, the one who has become an obedient servant to what her mother thought 'would be best for her' even if, by doing so, she has destroyed all references to who Rebecca Vickers is in the world. In the film she is a lost and bleached soul pretending to be a *grande dame* in a silent and lonely golden cage.

Through the manipulation of Maraea's hidden strings, the dynamic between the three women in the film becomes a constant confrontation of masked faces and buried secrets, a trap of *White Lies*. Inside that trap, each one of them is an antagonist to the other, and yet, at the same time, they all need one another to survive their actions and the consequences of their choices. In this triangular narrative structure, the three main characters in the film become active participants in the drama.

In the film, there is a completely new narrative element that triggers Paraiti's decision to go back to the villa of Rebecca Vickers and terminate the pregnancy. Paraiti is an impotent witness to the death of a young Maori mother and her unborn baby. Aroha and her child die in a Pakeha clinic, where Paraiti is humiliated by the matron in charge, and she is powerless when threatened with being sent to jail 'only for having medicinal herbs'. Not only that, but Paraiti is incapable of saving the most sacred symbol of maternity in the Maori universe: the whenua (the placenta) of the dead mother, which, instead of being returned to the land and the ancestors, is thrown on the rubbish heap of the hospital, as if it is a piece of garbage.

This event becomes the major turning point for Paraiti. It is the living experience of an undeniable reality that her world, the universe of her ancestors and the very possibility of continuity of her culture, is crumbling under the power of the imposition of a new and foreign law.

The burial of the placenta becomes, in the film, a major symbol; the symbol of identity, continuity and of restoration of justice. It is the greenstone door of peace, 'te tatau pounamu'.

THE CHARACTERS: TELLING WHITE LIES

In terms of the motivations that guide the actions of each of the three main characters in the story, there are important changes from the original novella *Medicine Woman* to the script and film *White Lies — Tuakiri Huna*.

PARAITI: THE MEDICINE WOMAN

An important difference in the configuration of Paraiti as a cinematographic character is that in the original novella *Medicine Woman*, Paraiti is not a mediator between the human world and the spiritual world.

In the script and the film, Paraiti grows from initially being someone who can only deal with minor infections of the body to a medicine woman who finds, precisely in the spiritual world, the answers to her doubts and the strength to cross territories of darkness and emerge from them with the purest and most sacred of all forms: the new life of a baby. This process of growth is the map and the compass to her journey through the film.

Another fundamental change in the film is the fact that Paraiti decides to save Rebecca's baby before she knows it is a Maori child. She fights for the life of the unborn child regardless of the colour of its skin. This was for me a crucial element to convey as storyteller and a vital condition to the configuration of Paraiti, as it is the ultimate expression of her human quality, a quality that gives her the moral stature and power to offer Rebecca Vickers redemption. This is a redemption that can only happen by Rebecca reclaiming her own identity and making peace with her motherhood. In the film, Paraiti gifts Rebecca Vickers the freedom that can come from the truth, from the possibility of making her own choices, and invites her to start a new life with her baby daughter, far from a life enslaved by white lies, under a 'tuakiri huna'.

REBECCA VICKERS: A SKIN BLEACHED WHITE

In the original novella *Medicine Woman*, pale white skin is a ticket for Rebecca Vickers into Pakeha high society. Bleaching her skin is a choice she takes, and ultimately uses, along with the sexual attraction of her youth, to 'catch the eye' of her rich and much older white husband. Her inner motivations are purely greed and vanity.

Contrastingly, in the film, the bleached skin of Rebecca is the most tangible reflection of the conflict which gives meaning to the film: the dilemma of identity.

Maraea's decision to bleach her daughter's skin is what, in her eyes, will save her daughter from the suffering that being a half-caste would cause her, yet ultimately it robs Rebecca of her true identity. Maraea's ways are wrong and twisted, but her ultimate motivation for bleaching Rebecca's skin is a wish for a better life for her daughter, 'not the life of a pariah' like her own. This, to me, encapsulates the very reason for creating the film *White Lies — Tuakiri Huna*.

In the novella, Rebecca's child is a result of a moment of adulterous passion. In the script, however, the child is the product of Mr and Mrs Vickers' marriage. Rebecca's conflict is not of infidelity, but rather resides within her own concealed identity and the fear of being discovered and rejected as one of the people her husband considers savages.

In the novella *Medicine Woman*, maternity is never a positive experience for Rebecca. Anatomically she carries her child, but emotionally she is completely disconnected and her only aim is to erase any possibility of existence for the baby.

In the film there is a transformation in the way Rebecca experiences motherhood. The bleached and destroyed woman who descends to the basement of the villa to give birth in the old traditional Maori way is a different person from the mother who emerges once the baby has been born. This is the transit of someone who has been living in absolute denial of herself and is finally redeemed by the restoration of her identity and her motherhood. It is her newborn daughter, a baby with brown skin, who finally liberates Rebecca from her past. This transit acquires, in the film, a sacred dimension that emerges from the presence of Paraiti, as a woman who walks in both the spiritual and temporal world.

In the original novella, Maraea holds on to her identity in a shy but significant manner. She prepares the birthplace for Rebecca in the old Maori ways and she tries to prevent the murder of her newborn granddaughter at the hands of Rebecca, who throws the baby into a river.

In the film, Maraea is ready to do anything to wash from herself and from Rebecca any traces of her Maori blood. Not only did she bleach her daughter under the promise that 'all will be better if you are white', but she is also the one who finds Paraiti and brings her to see Rebecca Vickers to perform an abortion on her — the abortion of her own Maori grandchild. In the film, the character of Maraea is not there to obey the wishes of her mistress, but to fulfil her own purpose: the preservation of herself and Rebecca from the life of the vanquished, the colonised — the people with dark skin.

In the last scene of the film between Maraea and Paraiti, the mother tells Paraiti, in a chilling and defeated voice, 'At least my daughter has a life, a house, land . . . That is much more than I ever had, Paraiti. Much more than what you have.' It is the terribly mistaken strategy of a mother, lost on the side of those who have been defeated and desperately looking for a way to ensure the survival of her daughter.

THE LANGUAGE

The use of te reo Maori and English in the film's dialogue becomes a clear and precise way to express the clash between two different worlds and, at the same time, celebrates the identity of the film.

Paraiti uses her language as an assertion of her identity and a tool to remind Maraea that no matter how properly she speaks in English she is and always will be a Maori woman.

One of the most fascinating and revealing experiences during the process of writing this film was the transition from the original novella *Medicine Woman*, mainly written in English, to the language of te reo Maori of the Tuhoe people of Ruatahuna in the screenplay.

In that process, every word acquired new and rich connotations. Through the deep knowledge of their language, the translators Kararaina Rangihau, Whitiaua Ropitini and Tangiora Tawhara took the dialogue to a place way beyond the functional purpose of naming, describing and communicating. They provided this film with a poetic cosmogony, music with multiple meanings and the organic, living expression of a profound, ancient, complex and holistic culture.

THE VISUAL GEOGRAPHY

The film has a diverse, powerful and vast source of visual inspiration. Each one of the many universes within this story has its own unique landscape and iconography, and each one is strongly attached to the individual identities of our three main characters. These territories are not only the natural environments for each of them, but they also reflect the worlds where they belong. They become an extension of the character's dramatic narrative.

Paraiti is an organic element within the green density of bush and humid light of the magnificent mountainous landscape of Te Urewera. Meanwhile, her marae is the sacred refuge where everything makes sense in her ancient understanding of life and the universe. A town created by the English settlers, with its shops, movie theatre and hospital, is the landscape within which Maraea wanders, sneaking from the corners, trying to blend into the Pakeha world. And, finally, the villa where Rebecca Vickers lives is a suffocating and closed trap . . . a cage that enslaves her, and a womb from which she will be reborn as a mother and where her identity will be redeemed.

THE STYLE AND GENRE

We have a film that touches intense, complex and violent issues. We chose to treat them with a gentle hand, seeking to create lyrical beauty not only in the images but also in the pace, the dialogue and the dramatic composition of the story.

In terms of the work with the actors, a naturalistic style, an almost whispering fashion of acting, creates the precise emotional tone for this film. This, I believe, allows the audience to connect with the emotional journey of the characters, beyond the brutality of their experiences.

The basic form of a psychological thriller served as an inspiration during the process of writing and imagining the film *White Lies — Tuakiri Huna*. This provided me with a simple and clear reference for how this film would function, the emotional place it would take us, and the tools with which it would be built. Two pivotal points of this film adaptation are the intense dynamics between the hidden faces and purposes of our three very strong characters and the narrative rhythm through which the unexpected mysteries of the film unfold.

THE FINAL CHANGE: THE END OF THE FILM

Cinema is a living, collective and utterly magical process. The duty and the pleasure of being a film director is to know how to listen to the inner voice of the story and allow it to flow towards the encounter of the characters and their true destiny, even if that means restructuring the narrative of the film itself. That is the indescribable miracle of filmmaking.

I was blessed to have the most fascinating change of direction in the story while shooting the scenes of the delivery of Rebecca's baby. The unique and amazing chemistry the actresses produced brought to the story a quality that was not in the original novella, nor in my script. The place where Rebecca, Maraea and Paraiti arrived at the end of their stories was the perfect closure to their journey and has given to this film the silent coherency it deserves.

I can only be grateful to all those who made this happen and helped me listen and find the way from the beginning all the way to the true ending to this film.

Dana Rotberg
Scriptwriter and director of *White Lies — Tuakiri Huna*
Auckland, Aotearoa New Zealand

WHITE LIES

DIRECTOR'S FINAL SCRIPT

Written by
DANA ROTBERG

Based on the novella
MEDICINE WOMAN *by* **WITI IHIMAERA**

EXT. MAORI VILLAGE BY THE EDGE OF A LAKE — DAY

PARAITI, a girl of barely 10 years, is seated on the ground in front of an orderly row of flowers, herbs and leaves of different colours and sizes, which are unfolded at her feet like a book. She is intently examining the design of the petals of a flower which she holds in her hands.

The girl gently crushes the flower with her fingers, and brings her hands to her nose. She inhales the aroma given off by the broken, moist petals.

Sitting beside the girl is her GRANDFATHER, who observes her with full concentration.

Not far from them, the girl's MOTHER and BROTHER are occupied sorting a pile of potatoes.

The grandfather takes a bunch of dark green leaves out of an old kete and offers them to Paraiti.

The girl smiles at her grandfather, takes the leaves from his hands and finds the

right place to put them among the rest of
the flowers and herbs lined up at her feet.

It is the sound of hoofbeats forcefully
hitting the ground that breaks
Paraiti's reverie.

The nearly idyllic silence is
extinguished by the cries of her
mother and the sound of gun fire.

In barely a few seconds, the landscape
is confused, filled with a desperate
disarray of people and animals racing
in all directions.

Paraiti sees a WHITE MAN thrust a
flaming branch into the small patch of
potatoes, which immediately bursts into
flame.

Paraiti tries to gather her bundle
of herbs, but the hooves of a horse
trample them.

Paraiti watches as her grandfather is
beaten and shoved along by TWO WHITE
MEN.

> GRANDFATHER
> *Paraiti!*

Suddenly, a hefty branch, licking with

brilliant orange flames, violently slashes across her face.

Stunned by the impact, Paraiti drops to the ground.

Galloping close to her, the group of white men disappear on their horses as quickly as they came.

The fury of the hoofbeats fades away, leaving behind only smoke and silence.

DISSOLVE TO:

The pile of potatoes is still smoking.

Close by, the burned bodies of the mother, brother and sister.

Not too far away, the body of her grandfather.

There is nothing left . . .

Very slowly, as if emerging from a bad dream, Paraiti opens her eyes. Her face is damaged; her skin is charred and burnt.

Shattered, Paraiti manages to stand.

She walks slowly, observing the

blackened carcass of what is revealed
to have been a small Maori settlement
that, until now, had basked in a vast
and magnificent landscape on the edge
of a beautiful blue lake.

Paraiti runs away.

EXT. FOREST — AFTERNOON

Her face caked with dark mud, a blinded
Paraiti runs, trying to find her way
through a field of tall grasses.

Her steps are guided only by the sound
of the water of the unseen lake.

Still blinded, she lowers herself down
the lake's bank, branch by branch,
gripping whatever falls into her hands.

Her feet sense the dampness of the
lake's edge.

She slows her pace, and thrusts her
face into the water to feel the lake's
cold embrace.

FADE OUT.

"WHITE LIES"

FADE IN:

EXT. MOUNTAINS / BUSH – DAY

As if the gods can't stop crying, an
immense rain falls over a majestic
range of mountains.

Hurled by a furious wind, the drops of
water rush from the tops of the ancient
trees all the way down to the tender
and humble moss that covers a narrow
path of dirt.

Everything is sprouting and green.

Paraiti is now an older woman. From her
forehead to her cheek, an enormous scar
marks her aging face.

Silently, she slowly walks through the
bush in the rain, her only company a
horse and a dog.

Paraiti observes the greenery. She
stops to pick some herbs, strangely
enlaced in the branches of a bush.

The work of her hands is subtle and

careful, and she makes sure she does
not disturb or damage the bush.

She murmurs, seeming to converse with
the plants as she tucks them away
inside her father's old kete.

Then she continues her languid journey.

EXT. TOP OF THE MOUNTAIN - AFTERNOON

Paraiti emerges from the bush, followed
by her dog and her horse.

In the distance, down in a valley, a
column of grey smoke rises from a small
village into the intensely blue sky.

Paraiti smiles and rides in the
direction of the village.

EXT. VILLAGE - EVENING

Paraiti and her animals approach a
small village.

EXT. GATE OF HORIANA'S
HOUSE - EVENING

Paraiti and her animals arrive at the

gate of a house surrounded by flowers.

A young boy runs to her.

> YOUNG MOKOPUNA
> *Kei te tomuri koe, Paraiti. Kua tae*
> *ke a Kuia Horiana ki te marae.*

> SUBTITLE:
> *You are late, Paraiti. Horiana's*
> *already gone to the meeting house*
> *for the service.*

Knowing she is late, Paraiti moves as
quickly as she can.

EXT. ROAD TO MARAE - SUNSET

Paraiti hurries towards the grounds
of the marae.

EXT. WHARE NUI - SUNSET

The PIRIHIMANA is just about to go
inside the meeting house when he sees
Paraiti running late. He walks back to
where the bell is and rings it again a
few quick times.

Paraiti approaches him as he gives her
a welcoming blessing.

As the blessing finishes, Paraiti
rushes to the entrance of the meeting
house.

INT. WHARE NUI - SUNSET

Aware she is late, Paraiti waits by the
door for a second. She glances about
until she spots a short, smiley, grey-
haired woman, HORIANA, who is saving
her a place.

WIREPA, the Tohunga, is waiting to
begin the service inside the meeting
house.

Paraiti sits beside Horiana.

Only then does Wirepa begin the
liturgy.

>WIREPA
>*Ka whakakitea a Te Matua Tangata*
>*ki te maramatanga pono, ko te*
>*maramatanga pono ko te Anahera.*
>*E kakahu ana ki te kakahu ma*
>*ano tona rite ki te hukarere,*
>*ana makawe he whetu piataata,*
>*he karauna koura i te upoko, he*
>*parirau ana, tona hanga ki nga tai*
>*o te kopere.*

*An angel appeared into the light
to the prophet Te Kooti, and the
angel was clothed in garments white
as snow, his hair like twinkling
stars, a crown of gold upon his
head, his wings the colour of a
rainbow.*

The people listen to the words of
Wirepa.

Women and men, old and young, are all
submerged in sacred silence.

WIREPA
*Katahi ka korero, E kore au e
whakarere i taku iwi, me taku iwi
ano. Koinei te maramatanga pono o
te Haahi, Kororia tona ingoa tapu.*

SUBTITLE:
*And the angel said to the prophet,
'I will not forsake my people nor
will my people be forsaken.' This
is the revelation of our faith.
Glory be to Thy holy name.*

Everyone in the meeting house repeats
the words, raising their hands.

WIREPA AND EVERYONE
Amine.

SUBTITLE:
Amen.

FADE OUT.

FADE IN:

EXT. WHARE NUI – MORNING

It's pouring with rain.

Horiana is seated by the entrance of
the meeting house.

Not too far away, Oti, the dog,
attentively waits.

A YOUNG GIRL limps from the meeting
house, holding a gourd bowl which she
has used to clean the wound on her
foot. She hands the gourd to Horiana
who steps away and pours the bloody
water into a larger container.

The young girl goes away and Horiana
sits by the large container, guarding
it.

INT. WHARE NUI – MORNING

Paraiti sits by the pou tahu, the

centre-front post of the meeting house.
By her side, on a low table, rest a
variety of medical utensils, some
clearly European, others Maori. Visible
are a mixture of scalpels, shells,
obsidian shards, clean rags, dried
gourd pots, potions, pharmaceutical
concoctions, herbs and compositions.

An EMACIATED OLD MAN, a CHILD with an
eye infection, a WOMAN with swollen
legs, a PREGNANT GIRL and a MATURE
COUPLE sit patiently waiting to be seen
by the medicine woman.

Paraiti reviews the waiting group. She
turns to the pregnant girl, AROHA, and
motions for her to approach.

The old woman with swollen legs reacts,
upset, but one sharp look from Paraiti
shuts her up.

Aroha, not even 14, is pale with sunken
eyes. In her childish, almost inaudible
voice, she tells Paraiti:

>AROHA
>*Koinei taku haputanga tuarua.*
>*Engari i whakatahe te mea tuatahi*
>*i mua noa atu i te tonga hanga o*
>*taku puku.*

SUBTITLE:
This is the second time I have had
a baby inside me.

Paraiti listens as she examines Aroha's
fingernails and hair, the texture of her
skin, the colour of her eyes.

PARAITI
He aha te korero a too whaea mo
tenei? He aha ia i kore ai e haere
mai ki too taha.

SUBTITLE:
What does your mother say about
this?

AROHA
E whakawhanau ana taku mama i a
ahau ka mate ia.

SUBTITLE:
My mother died when I was born.

With care and tenderness, Paraiti helps
Aroha recline on the cot and begins to
auscultate [listen to] the girl's lower
belly.

PARAITI

*Ehara koe i te tuatahi, otia
i te whakamutunga o te pani
whakawhaanau. Heoi ano, ko te mea
tika kia whakawhiwhia koe ki tetahi
kaiako. Ko ahau tena.*

SUBTITLE:

*Lay back. You are not the first,
nor will you be the last orphan to
give birth. All you need is someone
to teach you. I am that teacher.*

Paraiti begins to softly massage
Aroha's belly.

PARAITI

*O tatau ringaringa . . . he ako i
a tatau pepe ki te korero otira
maaku koe e ako. Na kua mohio koe
ki te korero ki too tamaiti, ki te
whakarongo hoki ki a ia. Ara ma o
ringaringa katoa eena ahua.*

SUBTITLE:

*With our hands . . . We teach our
babies to speak to us . . . And I
will show you how.*

Aroha gives her full concentration,
paying attention to the movements Paraiti
makes on her belly as if she wants to
imprint them in her young memory.

Paraiti invites Aroha to place her
hands on top of Paraiti's old and dry
hands.

Like fragile little paper ships,
Aroha's tiny hands make their way
around her belly.

> PARAITI
> *Ko te koopu o te wahine ko te ao*
> *tonu tena. Ko te kohao tena o te*
> *timatanga me te whakaotinga o nga*
> *mea katoa.*

> SUBTITLE:
> *The womb of a woman is the universe.*
> *The dark space where all things*
> *begin and are completed . . .*

Paraiti observes Aroha, then closes her
eyes in silence.

Aroha also closes her eyes.

After a few seconds, feeling unsure,
Aroha opens her eyes to check if
Paraiti still has her eyes closed; she
does. The doubting girl quickly closes
her eyes again.

Paraiti smiles and draws her hands
away, leaving the girl's hands poised
on her own belly.

PARAITI
*Ma too koopu e pae here too tamaiti
ki te whenua ki te iwi. Otira mo
ake tonu atu.*

SUBTITLE:
*Through your womb you will bond
your child to the land and to the
people. Forever.*

After a few seconds a smile comes
across the girl's face. Aroha laughs
aloud, happy.

AROHA
*Kai te whana pera i te whiore o te
ika!*

SUBTITLE:
*It's jumping around like a little
fish!*

Amused, Aroha opens her eyes to see
Paraiti returning a genuine, joyful
smile. Paraiti reaches out and softly
caresses the girl's face.

PARAITI
*Kai a koe ra te hua mana wahine
o te whaea! A, mea rawa ake kua
whakawhiwhia koe ki too tama . . .
ki too kotira raanei . . . Hei
tauawhi ki roto i o ringa.*

SUBTITLE:
Soon you will have your child
wrapped in your arms.

Aroha closes her eyes once again and
continues to massage her belly.

Paraiti watches her for few moments.

AROHA
Kia tata atu ki taku whakawhanau
mau pea ahau e awhina, e atawhai
hoki.

SUBTITLE:
You can be with me the day my baby
is born.

PARAITI
Ehe. Kaare e whakaae tia tena. He
ture pakeha.

SUBTITLE:
No. That is forbidden . . . It is
the white man's law.

The girl responds naturally.

AROHA
He aha ai kaare ano koe i mauhere
hia?

So why have they not put you in jail?

Paraiti deflects.

PARAITI
Ko aaku mahi he maama noa iho, ara he waewae pupuhi, maruu, poroiwi whati, motu . . .

SUBTITLE:
What I do is only the very simple things, swollen legs and bruises, a broken bone, or a cut . . .

Aroha turns her face away, disturbed and disappointed.

PARAITI
Kia kaha te kai, te katakata me te whakamahi i o ringaringa. Koina te ara e pakari ai to tu i te tu a te whaea otira e ora makohakoha ai too tamaiti.

SUBTITLE:
Eat well and laugh a lot and don't stop with your hands. Your child will grow strong and healthy.

She tenderly readjusts Aroha's dress, helping her back to her feet.

PARAITI
*He uaua tera ki te noho pani, te
kore matua, engari kai too taha
anoo o tipuna. Ahakoa kaare koe
I te kite i a ratau. Ka manaaki
tonu-hia koe e raatau, e marama
ana ahau ki tena.*

SUBTITLE:
*I know how hard it is not having
parents, but you have to know that
your ancestors are with you. Even
if you cannot see them, they are
here, taking care of you.*

Aroha tries to smile.

Paraiti returns her smile.

AROHA
Kia ora rawa atu, Paraiti.

SUBTITLE:
Thank you, Paraiti.

The girl's embrace catches Paraiti off-
guard. She is evidently quite unused to
such closeness.

Paraiti separates herself from the
girl's embrace and walks her to the
door.

PARAITI
Ka pai noa iho nga mea katoa.

SUBTITLE:
Everything will work out fine.

Before leaving the meeting house, Aroha
briefly turns her childish face back
to Paraiti and smiles at her with trust
and gratitude.

Paraiti watches the young girl leaving.
There is sorrow in Paraiti's smile.

Seconds later, Horiana pokes her head
in.

Paraiti is lost in her thoughts.

Horiana gives her a 'wake-up' sound.

Paraiti snaps out of it and then calls
Horiana to her side.

PARAITI
*Me mau o taua whakaaro ki te
kootiro ra. Me noho piri ia ki nga
waahine, kia aro ai ki te kaupapa o
te wharetangata. Maaku e waiho tena
kia koe.*

SUBTITLE:
*We need to keep an eye on that
girl. She must be among women
and will need attention with her
pregnancy. I'll leave that to you.*

Horiana nods, kisses Paraiti's hand
with love and respect and motions for
her to come out and have some fresh
air.

The two friends walk out away from the
meeting house.

PARAITI
*He ahua rite ia kia ahau, i te wa
i ahau e pena ana te pakeke . . .
Ahakoa kaare ahau i whiwhia hua.*

SUBTITLE:
*She reminds me of myself, when I
was her age . . . Although I have
never had a baby.*

Horiana smiles and gently rubs her
friend's hands.

HORIANA
*Koia koia, he aroha tonu kore ki
nga panipani!*

SUBTITLE:
All orphans remind you of yourself!

EXT. WHARE NUI - DAY

It is raining.

Paraiti and Horiana sit together.
Something in the body language of the
two women speaks to an old and close
camaraderie.

Horiana rises, preparing to fetch the
next patient, but Paraiti stops her.

>   PARAITI
>   *Kua rahi mo te ra nei. Kua pau taku*
>   *hau. Tukuna te korero ki te hunga*
>   *ra kua tata ahau te wehe atu ki te*
>   *taone nunui mai konei mo te hiahia*
>   *mea aa etahi.*
>
>   SUBTITLE:
>   *Enough for now. I'm tired. Let the*
>   *people know that I'm on my way*
>   *to town, in case someone needs*
>   *something.*

Horiana goes towards the meeting house,
leaving Paraiti resting outside. As
soon as Oti notices her master is on
her own, she approaches and leans her
snout on her lap.

Paraiti pats the dog's back.

HORIANA (OFF SCREEN)
*Apopo kai te hoki a Paraiti ki te
taone. Na, ko nga mea he tono a
ratau me tu ki tenei taha ko wetahi
o koutou me hoki mai apopo.*

SUBTITLE:
*Paraiti needs a rest. If you want
anything from town, tell me now.*

Amused, Paraiti overhears the old
woman with swollen legs grumbling her
protests.

OLD WOMAN (OFF SCREEN)
*Kua roa ke ahau e noho ana i konei,
Kua pau i ahau te ra!*

SUBTITLE:
I have been waiting here all day!

EXT. VILLAGE — DAY

Paraiti leaves the village, her horse at
her side and her dog following behind.

EXT. MOUNTAINS — DAY

Paraiti and her animals cross the
mountain range; its colours and
textures flow together.

EXT. DEVASTATED LANDSCAPE - DAY

The land is burnt and brown. No trees.
No life.

Paraiti walks slowly, as if crossing
a haunted territory . . . Oti is very
close by her side.

The whistle of a distant train pierces
the barren silence, bringing the sounds
of the town.

EXT. COMMERCIAL STREET
TOWN - AFTERNOON

Paraiti waits for the DOORMAN to open
the doors.

She leaves the shop carrying a few
packages.

Progressing through the urban streets,
Paraiti's gait is notably altered;
clearly this is not her world. She's
not intimidated but a cautious air
invests all her movements.

She walks across the street to the
movie theatre announcing a Charlie
Chaplin film. Not far from her, by the
doorway of a chemist shop is a MAORI

EMPLOYEE talking to MARAEA, a Maori
woman of about 50, wearing a fastidious
servant's uniform and white gloves.

Seconds later, a CHEMIST in a white
smock bursts from the shop. He turns
around and discovers the Maori employee
whispering with the servant, Maraea.

> CHEMIST
> (To the EMPLOYEE)
> *Ah! There you are! I don't pay you
> to be chatting on the streets! Back
> to work!*

Paraiti slows her pace and silently
witnesses how the chemist abuses the
two Maori women.

> CHEMIST (CONT'D)
> (To MARAEA)
> *If I see you again troubling my
> employees, I will report you to
> Mr Vickers! If you want to keep
> your job, you'd best stay away from
> here!*

For a brief moment, Paraiti and Maraea
are face to face a few metres apart.

Paraiti reacts and heads in the
direction of the theatre.

The chemist re-enters his pharmacy,
roughly pushing past his young Maori
employee.

>CHEMIST (CONT'D)
>(To the EMPLOYEE)
>*Inside!*

Once the chemist has disappeared inside
the shop, the employee runs towards
Maraea and with a quick whisper points
her finger in Paraiti's direction.

>MAORI EMPLOYEE
>(To MARAEA)
>*That's Paraiti! She could help you
>. . .*

After that, she immediately turns and
rushes back inside the chemist shop.

Peering back from around a corner up
ahead, Maraea's eyes furtively follow
Paraiti until she disappears into the
theatre lobby.

EXT. MOVIE THEATRE - AFTERNOON

Paraiti enters the theatre.

A big publicity stand announces the
screening of *The Kid.*

INT. MOVIE THEATRE /
LOBBY - AFTERNOON

Paraiti enters the theatre lobby.

Arranging her packages on the elegant
lobby seats, she waits for the ticket
booth to open.

Maraea appears and, half-hidden behind
the main door to the lobby, she looks
for Paraiti. Maraea meekly crosses the
lobby and heads towards Paraiti.

She takes a seat next to Paraiti and
speaks rapidly, casting her eyes low,
like a servant.

    MARAEA
    You must be Paraiti? May I trouble
    you?

Paraiti's only response is to listen.

    MARAEA (CONT'D)
    I have a mistress who needs a job
    done.

    PARAITI
    A tena he rite ano too wahine
    rangatira kia tatau?

SUBTITLE:
Is your mistress one of us?

MARAEA
*No . . . My mistress is Mrs Rebecca
Vickers.*

Paraiti doesn't take her eyes off
Maraea.

MARAEA (CONT'D)
*The Honourable Mr Vickers is
currently in Europe for business
. . . We are only recently arrived
here . . .*

The ticket booth is about to open and
a few PATRONS approach it and form a
queue. Paraiti seizes the moment to
excuse herself.

PARAITI
*Mo tetahi wa pea, haerere tonu mai
ai ahau ki konei, mo reira pea . . .*

SUBTITLE:
*Some other time perhaps. I come
here often, maybe next time . . .*

Paraiti stands, gathers her packages
and walks away from Maraea to take her
place at the end of the queue.

Seeing Paraiti leaving, Maraea follows
her.

Paraiti busies herself looking inside
her purse for the money to buy her
ticket. There is only one YOUNG WOMAN
ahead of her in the queue.

Paraiti is just about to pay for her
ticket when Maraea appears behind her.
Maraea seems lost and desperate . . .

> MARAEA
> *It is a matter of life and death.*

Paraiti hesitates, unsure of what to
do. After a deep sigh she agrees to
help Maraea.

> PARAITI
> *Ka hoatu e ahau tetahi haora ki too
> wahine rangatira.*

> SUBTITLE:
> *I will give one hour to your
> mistress.*

Back to her submissive ways, Maraea
responds.

> MARAEA
> *Thank you.*

Maraea lowers her eyes and whispers.

> MARAEA (CONT'D)
> *Follow me, but please stay back*
> *. . . It may be better that people*
> *don't know we are together.*

And without giving any time for more
conversation, she leaves the movie
theatre.

Paraiti follows her, a bit uneasy, a
bit curious and a bit amused by the
boldness of the servant.

EXT. ELEGANT STREET /
TOWN - AFTERNOON

In the elegant environs of the town,
the villas are large with green lawn
promenades, manicured topiaries and
flowers impressively arranged in
massive planters. A quite different
order of greenery than Paraiti knows
from the forests and mountains.

After Maraea turns a corner, she slows
her pace only long enough to confirm
that Paraiti still follows her. At
a distance, Paraiti walks slowly,
carrying her packages.

EXT. VICKERS' VILLA - AFTERNOON

Maraea disappears, first down a long
private drive then behind the elegant
two-storey white villa on the lush
property.

At the end of the drive, an OLD MAORI
GARDENER washes an elegant white car
that is parked in front of the entrance
to the house.

Paraiti goes down the drive but waits
at the main door, assuming that the
servant will open it for her.

After a moment, Maraea peers around
the side of the house at the service
entrance and impatiently waves Paraiti
to follow that way.

The old Maori gardener looks discreetly
at Paraiti as she enters the house.

> PARAITI
> (To the GARDENER)
> *Tena koe.*

> SUBTITLE:
> *Good day.*

INT. RECEIVING HALLWAY - AFTERNOON

Paraiti follows Maraea down a long
hallway that leads back to a large
reading room. The reading room shines
under a crystal chandelier, which is
switched on even in the light of day.

Paraiti walks past Maraea and places
her packages on top of a table.

> MARAEA
> *Be kind enough to wait here.*

Maraea indicates the entrance to the
reading room.

> MARAEA (CONT'D)
> *Mrs Vickers will see you soon.*

Maraea, with her eyes downcast as
always, steps aside to leave Paraiti
alone in the room.

INT. READING ROOM - AFTERNOON

The reading room is clearly a masculine
space.

The furniture is elegantly upholstered
and trophy animal heads hang from the
walls. The lamps cast light into an

infinity of mirrors of all types and
origins. At the back of the room,
facing a lovely fireplace, is a chaise
longue.

It is as if Paraiti has landed on
another planet. She is not intimidated
but she is alert.

She approaches a grand piano on which a
group of beautifully framed photographs
stands — a smiling adolescent girl
with a trophy, an old Irish family
portrait of a mother and father
sitting rigidly with a young boy, a
man standing proudly in front of the
gates of a factory, and a few others
of an exceedingly elegant couple in
different settings of European cities.
He is an older red-haired man; she is a
beautiful, and much younger, woman. She
is the girl with the trophy; he is the
proud man by the factory gates.

Paraiti selects one of the photographs
of the couple and carries it to a
window for a better view in the natural
light from outside.

Paraiti has pulled back the curtain to
get a better look at the photo, when,
from the entrance behind her, she
hears:

REBECCA
*If you have stolen anything while
you have been alone in the room, it
would be wise to put it back where
it belongs before you leave.*

Mrs REBECCA VICKERS is barely 25 years
old, with beautiful black hair and a
white, almost death-like pallor to
her skin. She is the woman in the
photographs. Despite her youth, her
presence is powerful, her beauty
mysterious, disturbing . . .

Ignoring Rebecca's comment, Paraiti
regards the photo in her hands and puts
it down.

PARAITI
What may I help you with, Missus?

REBECCA
My name is Mrs Rebecca Vickers.

PARAITI
Yes, I already know that . . .

At a languid, regal pace, Rebecca
crosses the room in Paraiti's
direction.

Each woman measures the other. Neither
breaks eye contact, more out of

curiosity than as a challenge. They
find themselves mere centimetres from
each other.

Suddenly, unexpectedly, almost
seductively, Rebecca lifts Paraiti's
chin with one hand. She clinically
observes the scar that runs across
Paraiti's face. With the index finger
of her other hand, the young woman
slowly and deliberately traces the
scar's line.

> REBECCA
> *I was told you were ugly, but
> really you are only burnt and
> scarred.*

Paraiti holds her breath. No one has
ever touched her face in such an
intimate way. It takes a few seconds
for her to recover her composure before
she can step away from Rebecca.

Turning away, with her back to Paraiti,
Rebecca unbuttons her dress, letting it
fall gently to the floor. Aware of her
beauty, Rebecca steps out of her dress
but keeps on her high heels. Under
the soft texture of a silk slip, the
skin of her back is so extremely white
that it appears to be almost weirdly
translucent grey.

Rebecca turns around to the front to
reveal her almost half-term pregnancy.

> REBECCA (CONT'D)
> *This is very simple. I am carrying*
> *a child I cannot have. I want you*
> *to get rid of it.*

Not taking her eyes off Rebecca,
Paraiti responds in the same cold
manner by which her services were
requested.

> PARAITI
> *And you assume I will do it only*
> *because you asked me?*

Rebecca grimaces, slightly annoyed
by what she understands as an
undisciplined answer from a servant.
With a patronising attitude, she
reclines on the chaise longue, takes
her time to get comfortable, and then
lights a cigarette.

> REBECCA
> *Maraea told me you Maoris have*
> *ancient ways. You are renowned for*
> *your clever hands. Those hands*
> *could secure the result I seek.*

Paraiti stands, fascinated by the
beautiful white body that lies poised

the length of the finely upholstered
chaise longue. But to her Rebecca is
no more than an alabaster sculpture and
Paraiti remains silent.

Rebecca tries again.

> REBECCA (CONT'D)
> *I will pay you handsomely both
> for your work . . . And for your
> silence.*

Paraiti expresses her words without
emotion – she is specific, dry,
precise.

> PARAITI
> *You are a Pakeha. Go and look for a
> solution with your doctors.*

Rebecca loses her patience.

> REBECCA
> *I cannot do that, as you may very
> well understand. In this hideous
> little town everyone is greedy for
> a reason to gossip!*

Paraiti turns around, and walks to the
door. She turns and looks one more time
at Rebecca, who remains reclined on the
sofa.

Rebecca looks at Paraiti with disdain and taps the ashes of her cigarette in an ashtray.

Paying her no more attention, Paraiti leaves both Mrs Vickers and the room behind.

INT. RECEIVING HALL - AFTERNOON

Unseen, from the hall, Maraea has witnessed the interview.

Paraiti stares at her harshly as she leaves the room.

Maraea follows her.

>   MARAEA
>   *If that baby is born, her life will*
>   *be destroyed . . .*

Ignoring what she has just heard, Paraiti picks up her packages.

Maraea stops her by holding the packages.

Paraiti shakes free of Maraea's grip.

>   PARAITI
>   *Kaua e ui mai ano!*

SUBTITLE:
*That is not my concern. Don't ask
me again!*

Holding her packages, Paraiti leaves
through the main door.

Maraea hears the impatient ring of a
hand bell and Rebecca calling her, but
she doesn't move; she just watches
Paraiti leave.

REBECCA (OFF SCREEN)
Maraea!

Only after the door has closed does
Maraea disappear in the direction of
her mistress's voice.

EXT. EDGE OF THE RIVER /
MOUNTAIN RANGES - DAY

Back in her world, Paraiti walks by the
edge of a powerful river. She observes
and gently touches the moss that covers
the trunks of the trees. She carefully
picks only those leaves that are
touched by the light of the sun.

Not far away, her horse, loaded with
the packages she bought in town, and
Oti the dog are waiting for her.

EXT. WHARE NUI – EVENING

Paraiti pulls up a stool at the entrance to the meeting house, setting down a small metal box and the packages she bought in town.

Horiana is there already and her YOUNG MOKOPUNA runs over and crouches by her side. He selects a couple of packages and reads in a loud voice.

> YOUNG MOKOPUNA
> *E rua nga iari kakahu whero. E toru nga kohao ma.*
>
> SUBTITLE:
> *Two yards of red cloth. Three spools of white thread.*

A WOMAN with TWO TAMARIKI at her side approaches.

> YOUNG MOKOPUNA
> *E toru hereni.*
>
> SUBTITLE:
> *Three shillings.*

The woman picks up the package and gives the mokopuna a bunch of coins. He counts them and places them in the metal box.

Paraiti reaches for a copper kettle.

> YOUNG MOKOPUNA
> *He tikera.*

> SUBTITLE:
> *A copper kettle.*

An OLDER MAN approaches and picks up
his merchandise.

> YOUNG MOKOPUNA
> *Whitu hereni me, te ono kapa.*

> SUBTITLE:
> *Seven shillings and sixpence. Good.*

The mokopuna receives some coins from
the older man and continues the process.
Others collect their packages as they pay.

EXT. BUSH - DAY

Blended with the most verdant parts of
the great landscape, Paraiti walks with
her animals.

Behind them, in the distance, a column
of smoke rises from the village.

They all disappear in the lush greenery
of the bush.

EXT. DENSE FOREST - AFTERNOON

Under rain, sheltered beneath a dense
canopy of giant ferns, a small rustic
tent seems to float on the white mist.

Made of a material that already seems
ancient - many rains have fallen over
its sides to wash away its textures
and what, long ago, were its colours -
the tent flies are wide open. Inside,
Paraiti has set out her healing herbs
and instruments. A cot and bench
complete the furniture.

The neighing of Paraiti's horse sounds
nearby.

Oti the dog curls up alongside Paraiti,
attentively observing her master.

Paraiti is working her fingers down the
throat of an ASTHMATIC BOY.

Paraiti finally manages to extract a
thick green wad of phlegm from the
boy's throat. She is triumphant.

The boy is wide-eyed in fascination.

> ASTHMATIC BOY
> *He pai noa iho te heri i tenei? Kia
> pai ai taku whakaatu ki waku hoa?*

*Can I take it home? I want to show
it to my cousins.*

Paraiti glances over to his MOTHER,
whose tacit reply with her eyes pleads
Paraiti to tell him 'no'.

Paraiti reads the impish look on the
boy's face. She enters the tent only to
emerge seconds later with a deep paua
shell in which she deposits the phlegm
then gives it to the boy.

> PARAITI
> *E i, ina ka mutu too whakaatu
> haere i too weriweri, whiua atu
> ki roto i te awa. Ki te kore ka
> nokinoki mai ano ia ki roto i too
> korokoro.*

> SUBTITLE:
> *Promise me that once you've shown
> your little monster around, you
> will throw it into the river. If
> not it will crawl right back inside
> your throat!*

The boy is stunned. Suitably impressed,
with his eyes wide open, he nods in
agreement.

Mother and boy leave the camp. She

reprimands him with successive raps on
the noggin.

The boy laughs out loud and runs off,
holding the paua shell in both hands
like a treasure.

Not too far away, a COUGHING OLD MAN
and his DAUGHTER are waiting for the
medicine woman to see them.

Bursting from the dense forest growth,
Horiana's grandson, sweating, races
toward the tent. He chokes out a cry a
few metres from the tent.

> HORIANA'S GRANDSON
> *Paraiti! Paraiti!*

Surprised by his arrival, Paraiti
approaches.

> HORIANA'S GRANDSON
> *He mea tono mai ahau e Kuia*
> *Horiana. Kua raru te kotiro hapu*
> *ra. Kei te rere te toto i waenganui*
> *i ona waewae. Mea mai ia kua kahaki*
> *hia e tana papara ki te taone. Ki*
> *te takuta.*

Horiana sent me to find you. There is trouble with that pregnant girl! She is bleeding between her legs . . . She said to tell you her uncle is taking her to town . . . To the doctors.

Paraiti listens intently. She gives calm and precise instructions to Horiana's grandson.

PARAITI
Whakarongo, mau e tuku iho taku kopuni. Katahi ka kawe atu ki te marae.

SUBTITLE:
Listen, you break my camp. Then load everything and take it to the village.

Winded and hacking, Horiana's grandson turns to begin his tasks. Paraiti rushes inside the tent, collects some herbs and sundries, then places them in her kete.

The young boy drags the horse towards Paraiti, who rushes him, impatient.

                    PARAITI
                    Awhinatia mai au ki runga i taku
                    hoiho!

                    SUBTITLE:
                    Help me on to my horse!

Horiana's grandson holds the horse
close to Paraiti, who, old and clumsy,
does her best to mount the beast.

                    PARAITI
                    (To OTI)
                    Haere mai, Oti!

                    SUBTITLE:
                    Let's go, Oti!

Paraiti gallops off as fast as
possible.

The dog runs behind her and her horse.

Soon they have become lost in the
forest.

INT. MEDICAL CLINIC – EVENING

In the hall of an urban medical clinic,
Paraiti sits next to Horiana. Not far
from them, a man with stains of fresh
blood on his shirt and trousers leans

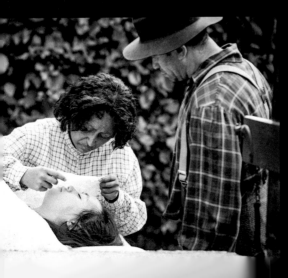

RIGHT
Cinematographer
Alun Bollinger with
Finn (playing Oti).
Location: exterior
Church of Scientology
buildings, Grafton,
Auckland.

BELOW
Director Dana Rotberg (centre) with Nancy Brunning as
Horiana (left foreground) and Jim White as Uncle Jim
(left background). Location: exterior Church of
Scientology buildings, Grafton, Auckland.

LEFT
Cinematographer
Alun Bollinger
at the camera
with focus puller
Bradley Willemse
(background) and
key grip Terry
Joosten. Location:
exterior Church
of Scientology
buildings,
Grafton, Auckland.

LEFT
Director Dana
Rotberg with
actor Rachel
House as Maraea.
Location:
Alberton House,
Auckland.

RIGHT
The camera
frames up on
Antonia Prebble
(playing
Rebecca).
Location:
Highwic House,
Auckland.

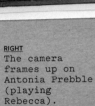

LEFT
White Lies crew
(foreground)
with Antonia
Prebble as
Rebecca
(background on
chaise longue).
Location:
Highwic House,
Auckland.

against the wall. He is AROHA'S UNCLE.
They all wait in silence.

With an energetic pace, the MATRON
comes down the stairs towards the
hall. She does not stop to talk.

Paraiti stands and approaches the
matron.

> PARAITI
> I need to see the pregnant girl.

Without any suggestion of sympathy, the
matron questions her.

> MATRON
> What is your relationship to the
> patient?

Realising she must avoid any hint of
confrontation, Paraiti simply answers:

> PARAITI
> Among our people, everyone is a
> family member.

With a frozen smile, the matron
replies:

MATRON

It's always the same with you
people. You are unable to learn.
Only when the sick ones are
incurable do you seek the doctor's
attention, expecting them to save
the patients. So much for caring
for 'family' . . .

Horiana approaches the matron and
shoves her back.

HORIANA

How dare you speak to her like
that! What do you know about
family, you barren old bitch?

Calmly, Paraiti turns and heads to the
door of a room, guarded by a MAORI
NURSE.

The matron turns and stops Paraiti
before she can reach the door handle
of Aroha's room. The matron removes
the bundle of herbs from the folds of
Paraiti's skirt.

Trying to recover the herbs, Paraiti
reaches for the matron's hand so
forcefully that it strikes fear into
the woman's heart.

PARAITI
These herbs will stop the bleeding.

Pulling rank and power, the matron
coolly warns Paraiti:

MATRON
I could have you thrown in jail
merely for having these herbs.

Before turning her back on Paraiti and
Horiana, the matron advises:

MATRON (CONT'D)
You should start praying for that
poor girl . . .

Paraiti's broken herbs in hand, the
matron disappears through an office
door at the end of a hallway.

Shattered, Paraiti is left facing the
Maori nurse who guards the door of
Aroha's room.

The Maori nurse looks down, but does
not move from her post.

The hall falls silent once again.

INT. OFFICE / MEDICAL CLINIC - NIGHT

The matron sits behind an austere desk.
Behind her is a crucifix, the room's
only decoration.

The Maori nurse and a YOUNG PAKEHA
NURSE are by her side.

Across the desk stands Aroha's uncle,
providing the matron with his niece's
personal information.

The matron writes down the details.

Paraiti is standing next to the office
door.

Utterly exhausted, they have clearly
passed a long and anguished night.

The young Pakeha nurse approaches
Paraiti, leans over her and offers her
heartfelt sympathy and condolences.

> YOUNG PAKEHA NURSE
> *We did everything humanly possible
> to save them . . . You must find
> your consolation knowing that they
> are with God and at His side . . .*

Paraiti's look cannot contain her contempt.
She turns away and addresses the matron.

> PARAITI
> *What must be done to remove our*
> *dead from this place?*

> MATRON
> *Which of you will sign the death*
> *certificate?*

Neither Paraiti nor the uncle can write,
a fact the matron knows well. Brimming
with scorn for Paraiti, she motions for
the Maori nurse to approach.

> MATRON (CONT'D)
> *Please sign here, nurse. And*
> *deliver the bodies to them.*

Paraiti's steely gaze holds on the
matron and her eyes are full of hate.

EXT. BACK DOOR / MEDICAL
CLINIC — DAWN

Horiana stands behind a rickety open-
tray truck. She folds a couple of
blood-stained blankets then places them
in the truck bed, making sure the clean
sides remain upwards.

From the clinic, a PAKEHA STRONG MAN
pushes a gurney on which rests the
body of Aroha. Across her chest rests

the inert body of her baby. Both are
wrapped in white jersey material.
Aroha's uncle walks by their side.

They go towards the truck.

Horiana uncovers Aroha's face and
places a white handkerchief over her.

Moments later, Paraiti exits the
building. She is profoundly undone.
Behind her, the matron follows.

> MATRON
> *Out!*

The matron gives her a push out the
door.

> PARAITI
> *I will not leave this place unless*
> *we take her placenta with us!*

Paraiti turns on her, almost desperate.

> PARAITI (CONT'D)
> *This girl and her baby will never*
> *find any peace unless I bring it*
> *back to the land! To our ancestors!*

The matron shoves her again, but this
time in the direction of waste-filled
barrels standing in a corner.

MATRON
Take whatever garbage you want.
Look for it. Take it away from
here!

Horiana can't contain her anger and is
about to react against the matron, but
Aroha's uncle holds her strongly by the
arm.

The matron returns to the clinic,
closing the door behind her. Once
safely locked inside, she watches
through the glass window.

Paraiti is standing right in front of
the barrels of waste. It takes her a
few seconds to know what to do . . .
She lifts the lid covering one barrel
and looks inside. She is pained by what
she sees. Clearly, there is no way to
recover what she is looking for. She
replaces the lid on the barrel.

Completely numb, Paraiti cannot react
any longer. Something deep inside her
is profoundly broken.

The Pakeha strong man, Aroha's uncle
and Horiana observe the scene. All of
them are equally disturbed.

The Pakeha strong man, who is deeply

moved, respectfully leaves the group
with their dead and disappears through
the doors of the clinic, which the
matron opens for him and quickly closes
again.

Horiana moves to Paraiti, still
standing by the waste barrels, too
stunned to move.

Horiana places her arm around her
friend's shoulders.

Paraiti and Horiana come over to the
tailgate of the truck. They take a last
look.

In the background, the matron observes
everything through the clinic door's
window.

Paraiti leans over Aroha's body and
recovers the small naked body of the
baby from the dead breasts of its
mother.

Paraiti's sorrow is immense.

She holds the infant to her own chest
and from the depths of her soul emerges
a profound and sacred chant.

EXT. RURAL ROAD - DAY

The truck makes its way along the rural
road. Tied to the back of the truck
trots Paraiti's horse.

EXT./INT. BACK OF THE TRUCK /
RURAL ROAD - DAY

Covered with a white sheet, the body of
Aroha lies on the back of the truck, in
between Paraiti and Horiana.

The dead baby is still wrapped in
Paraiti's blouse, between her old
breasts, close to her heart. She holds
the head of the dead infant with care,
as the truck bounces along the road.

Snuggled at her feet, her disconsolate
dog watches.

EXT. MAORI CEMETERY /
VILLAGE - EVENING

Wirepa walks alongside Paraiti. Horiana
follows a few steps behind.

PARAITI
*Ai kua hara ahau . . . kia koe, ki
taua kohine, ki tana pepe . . . ki
te hapu, a kia tatau katoa . . .*

SUBTITLE:
*I have failed . . . I let that girl
and her baby down . . . You, the
family and the people . . .*

Wirepa neither questions nor encourages
her in any way. He simply listens.

They approach the fresh graves of Aroha
and her baby.

PARAITI
*Kai te whakarerea enei ahua,
Wirepa. Me kimi ano e koe he
tangata hei tiaki i te iwi.*

SUBTITLE:
*I'm leaving all this behind,
Wirepa. You need to find someone
else to take care of the people.*

Wirepa stands, then places his hand on
Paraiti's shoulder as if she were still
a little girl.

WIREPA
*Ko koe ano hoki kai te mohio tonu
koe Paraiti.*

SUBTITLE:
Only you know what you have to do,
Paraiti.

Paraiti's gaze drifts away.

Horiana and Wirepa slowly make their
way out of the cemetery.

Paraiti stands alone by the grave, lost
in the anger and the emptiness of her
grief.

EXT. ELEGANT STREET – DAY

Four square on her horse, Paraiti rides
down the centre of the road toward the
Vickers House. Followed by her dog, she
owns the road.

EXT. MAIN ENTRANCE – DAY

Paraiti stands right in front of the
main door. She knocks and waits.

Unlike on her earlier visit, the house
now seems abandoned. The curtains are
drawn, the windows are closed. There is
a hollow silence.

A tired-looking and dishevelled Maraea

opens the door, her eyes downcast as
usual. Her hands seem wet and are
partially covered in a whitish paste;
she promptly wipes them off and hides
them away in the front pockets of her
apron.

    PARAITI
    Tikina to wahine rangatira, kia
    korero atu au ki a ia.

    SUBTITLE:
    I want to talk to your mistress.

Maraea stands aside to let Paraiti in.
Neither woman says a word.

Once Paraiti is inside, Maraea peers
outside and closes the door.

INT. RECEIVING HALLWAY – DAY

The home appears semi-packed up, as if
the occupants were on the verge of a
hasty move.

In one corner, a pair of open steamer
trunks sit half-filled. Paraiti kneels
beside them to discover the contents.

Rebecca Vickers appears at the back
of the hall. She walks slowly towards

Paraiti. Her hair is dripping with
water and her belly has grown so that
it is impossible to hide. Despite the
dark circles that ring her eyes and the
scraggly hair that partially covers her
face, she remains immensely beautiful.

Paraiti, still kneeling by the steamer
trunk, observes Rebecca's beauty.

Almost without paying attention to
Paraiti, Rebecca goes to the reading
room.

INT. READING ROOM — DAY

Paraiti follows Rebecca into the
reading room.

> PARAITI
> *Maybe I came back too late . . .*
> *I see you have travel plans . . .*

Rebecca's arrogance remains intact.

> REBECCA
> *If you've come to gloat, you can*
> *get out of my house right now.*

Each woman sizes the other up silently.

REBECCA (CONT'D)
Maraea said you had a matter of
interest to discuss with me.

PARAITI
Do you still want to end your
pregnancy?

Maintaining eye contact, Rebecca nods.
Each woman is trying to decipher the
other's true nature and intentions.

PARAITI (CONT'D)
I will begin tonight.

For the first time, and only for a
moment, Rebecca drops her frozen mask
of defence. Her face dissolves into an
odd expression of both pain and relief.
She walks slowly over and sits on the
chaise longue.

REBECCA
Tonight? How will you do that?

Paraiti speaks slowly, without emotion.

> PARAITI
> *With a herbal potion. You will*
> *drink it three times a day. I will*
> *massage your body and ask your*
> *child to leave it . . . . It will*
> *be painful, but in seven days it*
> *will be over.*

Rebecca recovers her harsh attitude and
takes a bell from the pocket of her
robe. She rings it.

Almost immediately Maraea appears in
the doorway.

Still keeping eye contact with Paraiti,
Rebecca asks Maraea:

> REBECCA
> *When does Mr Vickers arrive back in*
> *the country?*

> MARAEA
> *We are not certain, Madam, but he*
> *is expected any time this coming*
> *fortnight.*

Silent for a few seconds, Rebecca
evaluates the situation.

> REBECCA
> *You must take less time.*

PARAITI
Less time means more risk for you.

In a chilling and unexpected tone, the
servant breaks in.

MARAEA
*The risk is not of any matter. The
life of my mistress is already in
danger because she will not survive
her husband's rage.*

Somehow, the words of the servant
bring, from a remote place inside of
Rebecca, an old and painful shadow into
her eyes.

Silence.

PARAITI
*I know my business . . . Your heart
will not want to go all the way.*

Rebecca recovers her enormous self-
assurance.

REBECCA
I'm strong enough, believe me.

Rebecca looks around for Maraea.

REBECCA (CONT'D)
Put everything back in place.
Unpack the trunks. I want the
house impeccable.

MARAEA
Yes, Madam.

Maraea leaves.

REBECCA
Why are you doing this? What made
you change your mind?

Paraiti responds plainly, without any
arrogance, as a simple matter of fact.

PARAITI
This is my way of restoring some
justice.

The rules are clear.

INT. KITCHEN - DAY

Maraea shows Paraiti around the
kitchen, instructing her in the
household rules and schedules.

MARAEA
It is absolutely forbidden to enter
the second-floor bathroom, ever.

Without expecting an answer from
Paraiti, Maraea disappears for a short
time and returns with some old sheets
and a thin, worn mattress.

>MARAEA (CONT'D)
>*You may use the bathroom on the*
>*lower floor behind the staircase.*

Maraea places the mattress against the
wall next to the stove.

>MARAEA (CONT'D)
>*When you aren't working with*
>*Mrs Vickers you will remain in the*
>*kitchen. You have no permission*
>*to go into any other part of the*
>*house.*

For the first time, Paraiti reacts to
the endless talk of the servant.

>PARAITI
>*Te waahi ka mahia e au nga wai*
>*rakau kai ahau tera. Na he tapu te*
>*kaupapa nei, kaare e mahia e au i*
>*roto i te whare kai.*

>SUBTITLE:
>*Where I prepare my potions is my*
>*business. It is a sacred procedure*
>*and I can't do it in a kitchen.*

MARAEA
The instructions of Mrs Vickers
were clear. You are forbidden to
be in any other place in the house
but the kitchen unless you are
doing your job.

Irritated, Paraiti interrupts Maraea's
harangue.

PARAITI
He tino kuare ke nei koe. Nera?

SUBTITLE:
You are really ignorant, aren't
you?

MARAEA
It is not of my interest.

PARAITI
Me pono koe, mehemea ka hiahia koe
kia ora too wahine rangatira.

SUBTITLE:
It had better be, if you want your
dear mistress to survive.

Taking a minute more, Maraea passes her
hand over the sheets to make sure all
the wrinkles disappear.

MARAEA
What do you need?

PARAITI
*Inaara, ko tetahi waahi pai hei
tahu ahi, whakawhaiti i aku mahi,
kai ko atu o too te whare.*

SUBTITLE:
*I need a place to light a fire,
away from the house.*

Maraea looks at Paraiti, doubting for a
second, but finally she signals Paraiti
to follow and leaves the kitchen.

Paraiti follows her.

EXT. BACK GARDEN – NIGHT

At the back of the house there is a
small fire.

On a clean white tea towel placed on
the ground there is a big bath bailer,
a couple of pots filled with water and
several stones of different shapes and
sizes.

Not too far away, lying close to the
horse, Oti quietly watches Paraiti
organising in perfect alignment

- just as she did when she was a girl
- a display of various herbs, flowers
and roots.

INT. REBECCA'S BEDROOM - NIGHT

Rebecca lies on the bed.

Maraea opens the door from outside and
shows Paraiti the way into the room.

Paraiti enters with a steaming bowl and
some herbs and green leaves. She leans
over the edge of the bed. She fixes her
stare on Maraea and waves her out of
the room.

Maraea looks to Rebecca for approval;
receiving it, she turns to leave.

Once the servant is gone, Paraiti prays
in silence.

> REBECCA
> *I don't need any of your prayers.*

> PARAITI
> *They are for me, not for you.*
> *Although they will not hurt you.*

Paraiti sits at the side of the bed.

PARAITI (CONT'D)
Uncover your belly.

Rebecca unbuttons her robe and opens
it.

Paraiti dips the leaves into the bowl.

Mistrusting, almost fearful, Rebecca
observes what the old woman does.

Paraiti takes out some wet leaves and
places them on Rebecca's swollen belly
with slow movements.

Rebecca is tense but allows it.

Paraiti concentrates on pressing the
dripping leaves with enormous care on
specific parts of Rebecca's belly.

Paraiti offers Rebecca the bowl.

PARAITI (CONT'D)
Drink it when you are ready . . .

Rebecca takes the bowl in both hands
and slowly brings it close to her lips.
She is unsure about drinking it, but an
imperative gesture by Paraiti makes the
young woman swallow part of the liquid.
The bitter taste immediately makes
Rebecca want to throw up.

Paraiti covers Rebecca's mouth with
her hand.

A few seconds later, Rebecca drinks it
down despite its obviously unpleasant
flavour and puts the bowl back on the
dresser.

Rebecca vomits a yellowish liquid that
runs down her chest.

Paraiti cleans Rebecca's lips then
helps her recline again.

Spent, Rebecca closes her eyes.

For a while, Paraiti watches her sleep.
Despite her undeniable deterioration,
Rebecca remains strangely beautiful.
And fragile . . .

INT. KITCHEN - NIGHT

Maraea eats at the kitchen table.

Paraiti enters and looks at Maraea.

The servant eats silently, never
lifting her eyes from her plate. She
avoids any direct eye contact with
Paraiti, who observes her with great
attention.

PARAITI
*Ehia roa koe e mahi ana ma te
wahine nei.*

SUBTITLE:
*How long have you been working for
this woman?*

MARAEA
A long time.

Paraiti sits down at the table, very
close to Maraea.

PARAITI
*Ko too wahine rangatira kai te
aukati i a koe ki te koorero i to
taua reo?*

SUBTITLE:
*Is she the one who forbids you to
speak our language?*

MARAEA
*It is not forbidden. I just don't
want to speak it. That's all.*

Considering the conversation closed,
Maraea goes to the sink to wash her
plate, eyes downcast as usual.

PARAITI

*Ahakoa kaore koe e korero i too
reo, engari ka whakaaro nui ahau
kia kore e wareware i a koe.*

SUBTITLE:

*You may not want to speak it, but I
will make sure you don't forget it.*

Maraea leaves the kitchen.

Once alone, Paraiti drags the mattress
out of the kitchen and places it just
outside, in the corridor.

INT. HALLWAY – NIGHT

Paraiti rests on the thin, shoddy
mattress.

Outside, the dog howls softly. Paraiti
rises and opens the door to let the dog
in, who immediately curls up in her
skirt.

Paraiti lays out some blankets and
prepares to sleep. The dog is somehow
restless, at her side, close to her
body.

As Paraiti hums, the dog presses its
snout forward with anxiety.

                    PARAITI
                    Ina kaua e maharahara . . . Kai te
                    pai nga mea katoa . . .

                    SUBTITLE:
                    Don't worry, Oti. I know what I am
                    doing.

Paraiti pats the animal's rump.

FADE OUT.

FADE IN:

INT. HALLWAY - MORNING

Paraiti is asleep on the mattress.

Maraea enters the hallway on her way to
the kitchen and is surprised to find
Paraiti there.

Paraiti opens her eyes and props
herself up on one elbow to view Maraea
directly.

                    PARAITI
                    Kei te pehea to wahine rangatira?

                    SUBTITLE:
                    How is your mistress?

　　　MARAEA
　　　She slept all night.

Maraea goes inside the kitchen for
a moment and comes back with a tray
covered with a white cloth.

　　　MARAEA (CONT'D)
　　　Can I give her a bath?

Paraiti nods.

With an efficient and precise manner,
Maraea walks away, but, just before
leaving the hallway, she turns towards
Paraiti and looks at her with contempt.

　　　MARAEA (CONT'D)
　　　Why are you sleeping here?

Without waiting for an answer, Maraea
mumbles a disdainful comment to herself
and leaves.

EXT. BACK GARDEN - MORNING

Paraiti and Oti sit on the stairs of
the back porch.

Close to them is a tray with breakfast.

Paraiti pours some milk into a cup of

tea and offers it to Oti, who happily
drinks it.

INT. STAIRCASE - DAY

Paraiti walks up the mansion's
staircase and through the upstairs
hallway that leads to Rebecca's
bedroom. As usual, she carries the
steaming bowl and some dry herbs.

She hears a painful, suffocated cry.

Paraiti stops for a second and listens.

Instead of continuing on her way to
the bedroom, she silently walks in the
opposite direction, following the sound
of the moan.

INT. HALLWAY OUTSIDE BATHROOM - DAY

Paraiti stops across from the closed
bathroom door. Placing her ear close
to the door, she strains to overhear
what is going on inside. She hears the
muffled voices of Maraea and Rebecca.
Very carefully, she wiggles the door
handle and quietly opens the bathroom
door a crack to look inside.

Facing away from the door, Maraea sits
on a bench positioned alongside the
bathtub.

Rebecca is lying in the steamy bath
tub.

Silently Maraea rubs a thick, white
substance over the skin of the pregnant
woman, covering her nude back with the
creamy, white paste that she takes from
a bowl and repeatedly applies with her
fingers.

Rebecca's hair is pulled up at the
nape of her neck. The servant's hands
carefully apply the balm to every
part of Rebecca's skin, from her neck
to her shoulders and to her back. No
part remains uncovered. It is an odd
procedure, yet one that seems like a
ritual known to each woman: bitter
medicine, perhaps, but tolerated.

Rebecca seems to wear a strange white
mask broken only by the emptiness of
her black-ringed eyes, which fight to
hold back her tears.

Maraea stands up and goes to sit on the
edge of the bath, facing Rebecca.

Maraea rinses her hands in the bathtub

water. With a gesture, seemingly all
too familiar, she wipes away Rebecca's
tears with the back of her hand.

>   MARAEA
>   *Every time you cry, I have to
>   start again.*

Rebecca's expression is utterly blank
as she recoils from the clearly painful
application. She sheds silent tears.

Maraea, firmly but not harshly,
continues the process. She covers her
lady's face with the white paste that
Rebecca's thick, silent tears wash away
and leave tracks in.

Maraea again dips her fingers into
the white paste and once more covers
Rebecca's face.

INT. STAIRCASE – DAY

Paraiti sits halfway down the stairs.

Maraea appears at the top of the
stairs, carrying the bowl that held the
mixture used to cover Rebecca's body.

She sees Paraiti sitting on the steps
and continues down.

Just as Maraea passes by Paraiti's
side, trying to avoid her, Paraiti
tugs at Maraea's skirt to force Maraea
to sit by her side.

Maraea gasps in surprise and resists
the pull, but Paraiti tugs her even
harder until she sits down.

> PARAITI
> *He aha nga whakahaere o roto i*
> *te whare kaukau? He aha tena mea*
> *e pania na e koe ki runga i too*
> *wahine rangatira?*

> SUBTITLE:
> *What is going on in the bathroom?*
> *What is that muck that you're*
> *applying to your mistress?*

Maraea responds in a quiet voice.

> MARAEA
> *Mr Vickers likes his wife with*
> *smooth, white skin.*

Paraiti doesn't believe her. She
snatches the bowl from Maraea and holds
the stained hand of the servant for
a second. Paraiti looks at her, but
Maraea pulls her hand away.

Paraiti dips her fingers into the white

substance in the bowl, then smells it.
Feeling the white paste burn her skin,
she instantly wipes her fingers off on
her blouse.

INT. HALLWAY OUTSIDE BATHROOM - DAY

The bathroom door opens. Rebecca
emerges wrapped in a velvet-like
robe. She looks exhausted and somehow
defeated.

> PARAITI (OFF SCREEN)
> *Te mutunga atu kaare te wahine a*
> *Mr Vickers e urukehu, ka tere hemo*
> *ke ia.*

> SUBTITLE:
> *At this rate Mr Vickers won't have*
> *a white wife, he'll have a dead*
> *wife.*

Rebecca overhears the two women talking
on the staircase.

> PARAITI (OFF SCREEN)
> *Kaati te panipani i nga taruweku ra*
> *ki runga i a ia!*

> SUBTITLE:
> *Stop painting that rubbish on her!*

> MARAEA
> *You do what you must do and I do*
> *what I must do!*

Gathering back some strength, Rebecca
tries to recover her demeanour.

INT. STAIRCASE – DAY

From the top of the stairs, Rebecca
sees the two women. With what little
poise she has left, she dismisses them
both with a wave of her hand, as if she
were shooing away flies.

> REBECCA
> *What are you doing there? Get out!*
> *You look like vultures!*

Like a shot, Maraea heads downstairs.

> REBECCA (CONT'D)
> *I don't want to see you two*
> *gossiping again.*

From the ground floor, Maraea turns to
her lady at the top of the stairs, nods
submissively, then scurries into the
kitchen.

Rebecca walks towards her bedroom.

Paraiti rises slowly and follows
Rebecca.

INT. BEDROOM - DAY

The young woman picks up her pace as if
to escape from the healer.

Just before Rebecca can close the
bedroom door tight, Paraiti shoves her
crude, bare foot into the door jamb.

Rebecca shoves harder, like a cruel
little girl torturing an insect. But
Paraiti has suffered worse and refuses
to extract her foot.

Giving up, Rebecca relaxes her pressure
then turns to enter deeper into the
bedroom.

Paraiti enters behind her and closes
the door.

INT. DRESSING CLOSET /
REBECCA'S BEDROOM - DAY

Paraiti follows Rebecca into the walk-
in closet.

PARAITI

*Why are you doing all this? I
know women who would die to have
a baby . . .*

REBECCA

*You stupid woman . . . How could
you ever understand?*

PARAITI

*Do you think your husband will
throw you out if he discovers that
you are pregnant with another man's
child?*

Rebecca holds back any expression that
could reveal her feelings.

PARAITI (CONT'D)

*He will forgive you. You are
beautiful . . . Beauty can soften
the heart of any man. I have seen
it all before.*

Finished, Paraiti falls silent.

Rebecca draws close to Paraiti and
confides in a chilling and secretive
voice:

REBECCA

*So you think you have seen it all
before? You have no idea.*

Rebecca looks exhausted, defeated, almost old. She hasn't the energy to debate Paraiti. The tone of her reply carries none of her superiority. She is simply worn out.

> REBECCA (CONT'D)
> *We all have our wounds, Scarface ...*
> *Some carry them inside, like me.*

Rebecca looks at her directly. Paraiti sustains her gaze, almost intrigued.

Before Paraiti can respond, Rebecca's icy and authoritarian tone orders her to avoid further intimacies.

> REBECCA (CONT'D)
> *You have a job to do. Just do*
> *it! That is all you are allowed.*
> *Nothing else.*

Paraiti walks towards the door, but before she leaves the room she turns back to look at Rebecca one more time.

INT. STAIRCASE - NIGHT

Paraiti and Maraea walk up the stairs holding a couple of long wooden sticks on which a pot of steaming sand is balanced.

Aware that the balance of the pot depends on the coordination of their movements, both make an effort to work together and control the precarious task.

INT. REBECCA'S BEDROOM - NIGHT

Dressed in a beautiful long night robe, Rebecca sits on a chair, her legs apart.

The door of the room is wide open.

Paraiti and Maraea enter the room with the pot of steaming sand. Slowly, they approach Rebecca and they place the steaming pot with extreme care close to her feet.

Paraiti scoops some hot sand with a bowl, as Maraea pours boiling water on it. Steam comes out of the bowl.

Rebecca looks at the servant, who cannot hold her gaze and immediately lowers her eyes.

Paraiti uses the folds of her skirt to hold the steaming pot by the edge, and places it in between the young woman's legs, under her robe.

Rebecca reacts immediately to the
burning steam, but after a minute she
manages to control herself.

Paraiti checks on Rebecca to make sure
she can tolerate the treatment.

Never losing her composure, Rebecca
tolerates the pain with no expression
whatsoever.

Paraiti lifts the pot a bit higher
under Rebecca's robe.

This time Rebecca twists in pain.

Paraiti stops and puts the bowl on the
floor. Paraiti looks at Rebecca . . .
and leaves the bowl on the floor.

As soon as the door closes behind the
healer, Rebecca lets out a deep but
suffocated groan of pain and anguish.

INT. REBECCA'S BEDROOM - DAY

The bedroom is in shadow.

Maraea sits to one side of Rebecca's
bed watching her mistress sleep. She
pulls back a lock of Rebecca's hair
that has fallen across her sweat-soaked

forehead. It is a close and loving
gesture.

Paraiti enters slowly.

Sensing Paraiti's presence, Maraea
reverts to her solicitous servile
demeanour. She immediately pretends to
arrange the pillow where her mistress's
head rests.

> PARAITI
> *Awhina mai. Tukuna iho ia ki runga
> i te papa. Tikina he whariki me
> etahi miro.*

> SUBTITLE:
> *We need to place her on the floor.
> Get some clean sheets and blankets.*

> MARAEA
> *The floor? The floor is no place
> for my mistress!*

Paraiti doesn't show any signs of
patience.

> PARAITI
> *I te papa!*

> SUBTITLE:
> *I said, on the floor!*

Paraiti doesn't move, watching the
servant until she scampers out of the
bedroom like a centipede.

INT. REBECCA'S BEDROOM - DAY

Rebecca rests on the floor amid
throw-pillows and fine blankets. She
appears very pale with enormous dark
circles around her eyes. Her hair is
unkempt.

Paraiti is kneeling behind Rebecca,
facing her back. She is manipulating
the lower back muscles with gentle and
rhythmic movements.

In short order, Rebecca becomes
impatient.

>REBECCA
>*Don't waste time. You have to push*
>*it out, not pamper me!*

>PARAITI
>*Don't tell me my work.*

Undisturbed, Paraiti continues working.

>PARAITI (CONT'D)
>*I need to open your hips.*

From the corner of the room, Maraea
looks on in anguish.

> PARAITI (CONT'D)
> *Soon you will be begging me to*
> *pamper you.*

Paraiti applies forceful pressure to
the woman's hips, pushing, pulling,
freely tugging and manipulating
the pelvic bone structure in all
directions.

Suddenly, Rebecca cries out in pain.

Maraea hurries over to take her
mistress's hand in hers.

Rebecca turns to Maraea. Her look
is desperate, almost supplicating.
Maraea's face turns steely. She pulls
her hands back from Rebecca's and
returns to her corner of the room.

The lady and the servant remain looking
at each other, as if having a secret
and murky dialogue. It's only a few
seconds before Rebecca returns to that
place of intense pain.

Exhausted, Paraiti drops back and sits
on the floor.

PARAITI (CONT'D)
More tomorrow. This is too much.

Maraea dares not speak to Rebecca and
directs her comment to Paraiti.

MARAEA
*There is little time to lose. My
mistress will need time to recover
. . .*

It takes a long moment for Rebecca to
fully register the meaning of Maraea's
remark. She looks her in the eye,
contemptuously.

REBECCA
Get out of here.

Maraea obeys.

Once the servant has closed the door
behind her, Rebecca orders Paraiti.

REBECCA (CONT'D)
Keep on working!

Exhausted, Paraiti sits beside Rebecca.

PARAITI
Tomorrow, I said!

Slowly and with great difficulty,
Paraiti stands up and leaves the room.

Rebecca stays there, alone and broken,
like an abandoned rag doll.

EXT. BACK GARDEN - NIGHT

Paraiti is sitting by the fire. She
holds her head with both hands. Oti is
by her side, looking at her.

Paraiti looks at her dog and is about
to start talking, but can't. She covers
her mouth with the palm of her hand and
moves her head, unable to articulate
one word.

Oti keeps looking at Paraiti and
whines, as if she is trying to express
what her mistress cannot say.

Paraiti extends her hand and silently
calls her dog closer to her. She
caresses it with gratitude and love.
Both mistress and dog share, in
silence, the darkness of the moment.

INT. REBECCA'S BEDROOM - AFTERNOON

The door of the bedroom is blocked from
the inside with a chair.

Rebecca is still stretched out on the
floor, asleep. She appears very pale,
her hair is messy and unkempt. Her
beautiful face has become twisted,
greyish and dry.

Paraiti is kneeling at her side. She,
too, appears terribly worn out, spent.

Paraiti closes her eyes and quietly
whispers a prayer.

After a moment she begins to massage
Rebecca's belly with precise movements.

All of a sudden, Paraiti sees a
movement in Rebecca's womb. She closes
her eyes and, taking her time, follows
the movements coming from inside the
swollen belly with soft and gentle
hands.

A smile of joy comes to Paraiti's
face. She cannot take her eyes off the
hypnotic movements inside Rebecca's
womb.

After a moment, delicately, she places

Rebecca's hands on her own pregnant belly.

Paraiti waits.

Nothing happens.

Paraiti places her hands over Rebecca's hands like she did in the past with Aroha, as if she will guide them.

No movement in the belly.

Paraiti places Rebecca's hands at the sides of her body and observes. There is no more movement coming from the womb.

Paraiti puts her own hands back on Rebecca's belly, and she feels a clear jump.

Rebecca continues to sleep. Her enormous belly moves.

For the first time, we see Paraiti totally happy, relieved.

Always following the movements coming from Rebecca's womb, in a perfect pas de deux, Paraiti's hands move softly.

She sings a peaceful, quiet, sacred lullaby.

FADE OUT.

FADE IN:

INT. HALLWAY OUTSIDE
REBECCA'S BEDROOM - NIGHT

Maraea carries her mistress's dinner
tray in her hands. She tries to open
the door to the room, but she can't.

She pushes the door with her hips with
no success.

INT. REBECCA'S BEDROOM - NIGHT

Paraiti has fallen asleep by Rebecca's
side. Her hands are still in contact
with Rebecca's belly.

The noise of the door being pushed
wakes her up.

She goes to the door and drags the
chair away and opens the door.

INT. HALLWAY OUTSIDE
REBECCA'S BEDROOM - NIGHT

Maraea tries to get inside the bedroom,

but Paraiti closes the door and stands in front of her, blocking her way in.

> MARAEA
> What are you doing? If I were you,
> I would be very careful, Paraiti.
> Let's be very clear about this!

Paraiti is calm and peaceful. Somehow she knows she doesn't have any more need to confront Maraea.

> PARAITI
> You want to be clear about this?
> You want it in English? Fine, let's
> be clear once and for all. What I
> am doing and what I will keep on
> doing is everything in my power to
> bring this child to life! That is
> what I have always been doing in
> that room!

Maraea is paralysed.

> PARAITI
> Whether your mistress survives is
> no concern of mine, but whether the
> child comes dead or alive, either
> way, I keep it. Now you know the
> price of my work!

With that, Paraiti leaves the room.

Maraea cannot contain her surprise. She goes inside the bedroom, and closes the door silently.

FADE OUT.

FADE IN:

INT. BATHROOM – DAY

Rebecca, pale and exhausted, is stretched out in the tub. She can hardly hold the position of her body.

The bath water is milky white except for a tiny red cloud floating above her pubic area.

She hears the rushing footsteps of Maraea and Paraiti.

> MARAEA (OFF SCREEN)
> *She is in the bathroom . . . The labour pains have started!*

Paraiti rushes inside, followed by the servant, who stands in the doorway.

With the little strength that is left in her, Rebecca casts a sharp, hateful look at Paraiti.

REBECCA
*Who do you think you are, you old
witch? You have no right to demand
anything!*

Ignoring her, Paraiti approaches the
bath, kneels beside it and places her
hand on Rebecca's wet crotch.

PARAITI
*You are the one who is in no
position to demand . . . Its life,
or yours . . . I decide!*

REBECCA
*I don't care much for my life if
this creature lives! It will haunt
me forever!*

Maraea comes over, sits by the edge of
the bath tub at Rebecca's side, then
takes the young woman's head in her
hands to kiss her forehead.

MARAEA
*You can't give up now! I told you.
Let her have the child if that is
what she wants!*

Rebecca shuts up, but refuses, shaking
her head 'no'. Tears roll down her
face.

MARAEA (CONT'D)
Think how far you have come . . .
Think about what you have endured
to have a life of dignity.

Rebecca looks down at her pregnant body
covered with white paste, submerged
in the water. With a bitter smile, she
turns to face Maraea.

REBECCA
Dignity? What do you see here in me
that reminds you of anything like
dignity, Mother?

Holding Rebecca's belly, Paraiti is in
shock. She cannot move.

PARAITI
I pehea mai koe?

SUBTITLE:
What did you just say?

Although Rebecca is talking to Paraiti,
her eyes are locked right into Maraea's
eyes.

REBECCA
She has bleached me! Since I can
remember she has bleached my skin
. . .

Paraiti is appalled. She can hardly
react to what she is hearing.

>REBECCA (CONT'D)
>*She said that it would be better*
>*if I was white . . . .*

Paraiti can hardly believe what she
is hearing. She looks at Maraea, who
immediately lowers her eyes.

>PARAITI
>(To MARAEA)
>*Tenei tamaiti he mokopuna nau . . . ?!*

>SUBTITLE:
>*The baby is your grandchild . . . !?*

Paraiti hastens towards the bathroom
door.

Maraea runs after and blocks her exit,
stopping her.

>MARAEA
>*You cannot run away now! It's too*
>*late . . . You are part of it now!*

Paraiti gathers all the equanimity she
is capable of.

> PARAITI
> *I am not going anywhere! Listen to*
> *me carefully.*

Rebecca's contractions begin and she
cries in pain.

Paraiti states with unquestionable
authority:

> PARAITI (CONT'D)
> *Ka whakawhanau too tamaahine pena i*
> *a koe i te wa i whakawhanau ai koe.*
> *Hoatu koe whakaritea nga ahua moona*
> *pena tonu i te whakarite a too*
> *whaea mou, to kuia me nga wahine*
> *katoa o to taha ukaipo mai rano!*

> SUBTITLE:
> *Your daughter is going to give*
> *birth just like you did. Go*
> *and prepare everything the way*
> *your mother did for you, your*
> *grandmother and all of our women*
> *before her!*

Stunned by Paraiti's fury and out
of options, Maraea rushes from the
bathroom to do as she is told.

Rebecca has another contraction.

Paraiti rushes toward the bath, grabs a

towel and gets inside the tub herself.
She covers Rebecca's shoulders and
locks her arms around Rebecca's nude
body.

Unable to resist anymore, Rebecca lets
herself rest in Paraiti's arms.

Viscous remains of the white concoction
still drip from her ghost-like skin.

INT. STAIRCASE – DAY

With great difficulty, Paraiti and
Rebecca descend the stairs. Rebecca
supports herself by hanging onto
Paraiti's ample, crooked frame.

INT. HALLWAY – DAY

Paraiti and Rebecca slowly walk through
the hallway, entangled in a clumsy,
awkward, but undeniably bonded embrace.

At the far end of the hallway, alone,
Maraea sees them come. Without paying
any attention to the servant, Paraiti
and Rebecca disappear behind a door.
Maraea follows them and closes the door
behind her.

FADE OUT.

FADE IN:

INT. BASEMENT — DUSK

The cellar, a small, damp hole,
barely illuminated by the stove fire,
resembles a tight and bloody womb.

The space is filled with the deep sound
of Paraiti chanting a karakia, inviting
the unborn to come to life, to the land
of the ancestors and to be redeemed
by the love of the people and relieved
from all pains.

Not too far away, Rebecca can hardly
stand on her feet. Maraea, seated on
the dirt floor by her side, is holding
her exhausted daughter.

Paraiti extends her arms towards
Rebecca's belly and, for a second, the
three bodies gather together in such
close contact that it makes an organic
but murky cocoon.

When Rebecca feels the hands of the
healer on her skin, she separates
herself from the support of her mother,
as if guided by the invisible strings

of a master puppeteer, and leans over Paraiti.

Paraiti carefully begins to caress the swollen belly, searching for signs of life inside the womb.

Through a small window, the rays of the moon cast across Rebecca's face. She holds the head of the medicine woman in her hands and, from a place unknown to her, beyond all her possible memories, a weak and broken voice follows the song of the ancient prayer.

FADE OUT.

FADE IN:

INT. BASEMENT — NIGHT

Rebecca supports herself by gripping an overhead ceiling rafter. The position allows her slack body to droop in a squatting position with her knees wide apart.

On her knees facing Rebecca, Paraiti alternates between applying the soft massaging movements of her hands with heavier pressure on Rebecca's womb.

Rebecca cries in pain and drops, limp.
Maraea runs to her side and, holding
her from behind, supports all her dead
weight.

Paraiti works desperately. She searches
for signs of life from the unborn baby.
She cannot find any, but is undeterred.
Placing her lips on Rebecca's belly,
over her womb, she whispers to the
baby.

Nothing.

Paraiti strokes Rebecca's stomach, then
waits with quiet hands. Seconds later,
she continues her massage.

The labour pains grow, making Paraiti's
work more desperate.

FADE OUT.

FADE IN:

INT. BASEMENT - DAWN

The three women are spent. The birth
has been prolonged.

Paraiti now applies pressure with her
knees.

Rebecca cries out in pain. By this
time, she recoils from everything.

Paraiti listens more closely to the
baby in the womb.

With extreme care, she places her hands
between Rebecca's legs and receives the
tiny body of a BABY GIRL . . . Her skin
is brown!

Paraiti's face shines, overcome with
joy.

From a cord hanging between her
breasts, Paraiti takes a small obsidian
stone filed into a blade. She severs
the umbilical cord that still unites
Rebecca to the newborn body.

>   PARAITI
>   (To REBECCA)
>   *You have a daughter . . . !*

Nearly unconscious now, Rebecca lets
her body drop. Maraea carefully rests
her on the floor.

Holding the baby with both hands right in
front of her face, Paraiti gently presses
her forehead against the baby's and, with
a long and deep hongi, she welcomes the
baby to life and to the land.

With a subtle, almost imperceptible
breath, followed by a quiet small cry,
the infant reacts.

Paraiti opens her blouse and warms the
baby girl against her old and empty
breasts.

Maraea embraces Rebecca, as if she
could hold in her arms all the
sufferings of her child. Not unlike a
distorted 'Pieta' . . .

FADE OUT.

FADE IN:

INT. BASEMENT – DAY

The first light of dawn enters through
the little window.

Rebecca, beyond exhaustion, rests in
her mother's lap with her eyes closed.

Paraiti then holds the baby very close
to Rebecca's breast and places the
little mouth onto the nipple.

The newborn hesitates a few moments
before taking to Rebecca's breast but,
once she does, she sucks vehemently.

● 234

For a few seconds, the three women are
held together, surrounding the tiny
body of the baby girl.

All is silent, apart from the sound
of the baby sucking the mother's milk.

Rebecca turns her face away from the
child, totally disengaging herself from
what is happening between herself and
the baby, as if she doesn't want to be
in her own body anymore.

Making sure the baby is held securely
by Maraea, Paraiti moves away, collects
the placenta from the dirt floor and
carefully places it in a piece of clean
cloth.

Maraea strokes Rebecca's face.

> MARAEA
> *It's all over. It's all over . . .*
> *In a few months you will not even*
> *remember any of this . . .*

Appalled by Maraea's words, Paraiti
turns towards her.

> PARAITI
> *I te wa e no te ana te tamaiti i*
> *te u o toona whaea, kaua koe e*
> *whakatata mai.*

SUBTITLE:
*As long as this child is on her
mother's breast, you will not come
near them.*

EXT. BACK GARDEN – DAY

Paraiti holds the cloth containing
Rebecca's placenta. The baby is tightly
wrapped across her breasts.

She kneels by the roots of a tree and
digs a hole with her hands. She places
the placenta in the hole and covers it
with soil.

Paraiti prays, having given back to the
earth, the origin of life.

> PARAITI
> *He honore, he kororia, he
> maungarongo ki te whenua, he
> whakaaro pai ki nga tangata katoa,
> amine. E taku kaiwhakaora, tenei te
> tuku atu i te whenua ki te whenua,
> kia heria mai, kia kawea mai e koe
> te mauri o tera o nga tamaiti i
> mate mai, kia paiherehia raua, kia
> hoki atu ano ki te wahi i ahu mai
> raua. Kororia ki to ingoa tapu.
> Amine.*

*Glory be to Thy holy name. The
giver of life. I commit this
placenta to the land. That it may
be joined to the spirit and the
life force of the mother and the
baby lost in the past and together
they may return to the womb of the
land, the source of the universe.
Glory be to Thy holy name. Amen.*

Not too far away, half-hidden behind
the veranda of the big villa, Maraea
quietly observes the ritual burial of
her granddaughter's placenta.

INT. BASEMENT – EVENING

In a corner of the basement, Paraiti
is seated of an old armchair. She is
cradling the newborn girl in her arms.
Close to her is an organised and tidy
arrangement of herbs, leaves and clean
tea towels.

Paraiti inspects with care the wound of
the umbilical cord on the baby, then
takes a bundle of fresh green leaves,
puts them in her mouth and chews them.
Once she is sure the mash of leaves
is soft and moist, she applies it
carefully to the wound.

Paraiti covers the wound with fresh
leaves and finishes dressing the baby
in strips of white cloth.

INT. BASEMENT - NIGHT

Rebecca sleeps, sprawled out on the
floor, her limp body partially covered
by blankets.

Paraiti sleeps peacefully in the
armchair. On top of her, nestled
between her breasts, but perfectly
wrapped in clean rugs, rests the
newborn.

The amber light of a small fire
flickers with its warmth on them.

Right by the outside of the doorway
that frames the basement entrance,
huddled in her own body, sleeps Maraea.

FADE OUT.

FADE IN:

INT. BASEMENT - MORNING

The basement area is now clean and
tidy, luminous.

Paraiti opens her blouse and warms the baby girl against her old and empty breasts.

She massages the little body, admiring its perfection.

> PARAITI
> *Too purotu . . . me too ataahua hoki!*

> SUBTITLE:
> *How perfect . . . and how beautiful you are!*

Maraea, sitting on the stairs, forbidden to come any closer, watches Paraiti and the baby.

The baby begins to cry, searching in Paraiti's dry breasts for the milk she needs.

Paraiti holds the child in her embrace and carries her to where Rebecca, still sleeping, lies helpless across the mattress.

Paraiti opens the camisole that covers Rebecca, and places the baby near her breast. Rebecca opens her eyes and reacts with fear and disgust to the presence of the baby.

With her left hand Paraiti positions
Rebecca's nipple, ensuring that the
baby has a firm hold.

> PARAITI
> *You may not want to feed this baby,*
> *but this baby will live.*

Rebecca cries.

The baby cries.

Paraiti is broken by the pain of the
mother and the child. Overwhelmed by
a feeling of impotence, she confronts
Maraea.

> PARAITI (CONT'D)
> *Titiro, nau tera mahi, koina rawa*
> *too hiahia? Hoake! E puta.*

> SUBTITLE:
> *This is your doing! Are you happy*
> *now? Is this what you wanted? Go*
> *and make yourself useful! Get out.*

Maraea disappears up the stairs.

INT. KITCHEN - DAY

Maraea cooks at the stove. She cries in
silence.

EXT. FRONT GARDEN - DAY

Still in the sling, Paraiti holds the
baby close to her chest.

Lost in despair, not knowing how to
repair what she now believes is beyond
repair, she kneels by the roots of the
tree where only a few days before she
buried the placenta.

> PARAITI
> *Tohuhia mai, me aha ahau! Me pehea
> e ora ai i ahau te tamaiti nei? E
> te Matua . . . ? Tupuna ma . . . ?
> Awhina mai!*

> SUBTITLE:
> *Tell me what to do! How can I help
> this child? Parents, ancestors . . . ?
> Help me!*

Motionless, Paraiti closes her eyes.

INT. BASEMENT - DAY

Rebecca is sitting on a dilapidated
armchair, all alone in the basement,
like the forgotten queen of a defeated
kingdom.

INT. HALLWAY - DAY

Maraea kneels, scrubbing the wooden
floor. A bucket filled with water sits
by her side.

Paraiti enters with the baby in her
arms.

Maraea stops what she is doing and
raises her face to look up at Paraiti.

> MARAEA
> *It takes more than having a*
> *baby in your arms to be a mother*
> *Paraiti . . . You would never know*
> *about how far one is ready to go*
> *for them . . . That can be known*
> *only to those of us who have had*
> *our child growing inside our wombs*
> *. . . And that will never be your*
> *case . . .*

Paraiti resents what Maraea has said.
She is about to answer, but she
contains herself and just looks back
at Maraea with disdain. She covers the
baby with her body and moves carefully
to one side to pass by the servant.

MARAEA (CONT'D)
You think you're so pure, Paraiti
. . .But you and me . . . we are
not so different.

That comment stops Paraiti. She turns
to face Maraea for a second.

PARAITI
Katahi koe ka tino hee rawa atu.

SUBTITLE:
You couldn't be more wrong!

Then Paraiti disappears through the
door with the baby, on her way to the
basement.

INT. BASEMENT – DAY

Still disturbed by Maraea's words,
Paraiti goes down to the basement.

Rebecca has fallen asleep on the sofa.

Paraiti quietly approaches Rebecca
and sits by her side, holding the
baby close to her own heart. After
long seconds, Paraiti moves towards
Rebecca and gently awakens her with a
soft nudge. She holds the baby out to
Rebecca.

Half-asleep, Rebecca is confused. She
looks at Paraiti, puzzled.

Paraiti opens Rebecca's blouse,
undresses the baby, and uses Rebecca's
hands to wrap the baby in her own arms,
skin on skin.

Rebecca takes the baby in her arms in
an embrace she is not ready for at all
. . .

Rebecca does not move.

Paraiti repositions the baby, softly
making the contact more intimate.

Paraiti recites a karakia to bless them
all.

>PARAITI
>*E te kaiwhakaora, e tuku atu nei
>i enei inoi ki a koe, kia aroha
>mai koe, ki tenei o au i roto i
>ona mamae, nga mauhere i runga
>i a ia, whakakotahihia raua e te
>kaiwhakaora, aroha mai ki ona
>whakapapa, kia noho tahi, kia kaua
>hoki raua e wareware ki a koe te
>Kaiwhakaora, aroha mai ra, aroha
>mai kia ora tenei whakapapa, aianei
>mo ake tonu atu. Amine.*

I surrender myself in prayer,
and I ask to heal the pain that
surrounds this woman. Let the
sacred bond between the child
and her mother be redeemed. And
let it be blessed with Your love.
They shall never forget Your
presence nor You theirs. Now and
forever. Amen.

From a profound and old longing,
Rebecca allows the blessing of Paraiti
to soothe the buried wounds of her skin
and her heart.

INT. KITCHEN - DAY

Maraea concentrates on folding with
precision a never-ending pile of white
linen serviettes.

Paraiti enters the room with the sole
and explicit purpose of confronting
her.

> PARAITI
> *Kore rawa atu ahau i mohio he aha*
> *i taea ai e koe te rukahu i nga*
> *tau ko pahemo . . . Tata tonu*
> *koe ka puta . . . Engari kaore i*
> *tutuki . . .*

I don't know how you managed to deceive everyone for so many years . . . You almost got away with it . . . But you did not.

Maraea keeps on folding serviettes obsessively, as if by continuing her absurd task she could hold on to a world that she refuses to accept has just crumbled.

FADE OUT.

FADE IN:

INT. BASEMENT — EVENING

Paraiti clears the basement with water and a prayer.

Rebecca stands in the middle of the room with her baby in her arms.

Maraea, an exiled ghost, sits far away, at the top of the stairs.

Once Paraiti has finished her ritual, she holds Rebecca with much care and tenderness and helps her walk towards the stairs.

Rebecca walks slowly, not yet sure if she is ready to go back up to the house.

Paraiti gently encourages her.

Step by step, Rebecca goes up the stairs.

Just before passing by her mother, Rebecca turns her body away, preventing any possible contact between Maraea and her baby.

Rebecca leaves the basement with her baby.

Maraea follows.

INT. CORRIDOR - EVENING

Rebecca walks away with the baby in her arms.

Maraea follows, hastening her walk. She is about to put an arm around Rebecca's shoulder, but her daughter's sharp look stops her.

> REBECCA
> *Don't you have duties?*

Maraea freezes, her arm falls limp.

Trying not to break down in her own grief, Rebecca leaves with the baby.

No more a mother to her daughter, but now a servant to her master, Maraea obediently goes back to the kitchen.

EXT. BASEMENT - NIGHT

A fire burns in the incinerator.

Nearby are familiar objects from the birth like the mattress and blankets.

Paraiti brings the objects to the fire, places them in the flames and watches until all the objects are consumed.

FADE OUT.

FADE IN:

INT. REBECCA'S BEDROOM - NIGHT

Rebecca is in her bedroom, comfortably reclined in her marital bed, holding her daughter in her arms. Although she is back in the world where she belongs, she looks more lost than ever.

Paraiti sits on a corner of the bed,

watching the mother and daughter. She
reaches out and picks up a photograph
of Rebecca and her husband.

> PARAITI
> *Is he the father?*

Rebecca turns to look at Paraiti. For
the first time there is no conflict
between the two women.

> REBECCA
> *Yes, he is the father.*

> PARAITI
> *Does he know?*

Rebecca denies with a silent gesture.

> REBECCA
> *He doesn't like savages.*

Incredibly sad, Rebecca looks back at
the little face of her baby.

INT. CORRIDOR - NIGHT

Paraiti prepares to sleep. Oti is by
her side.

The old woman can't take her mind off
Rebecca's words.

INT. REBECCA'S BEDROOM - NIGHT

Rebecca is lying on her bed. Beside her, the baby lies in absolute peace, trust and innocence.

Rebecca stares at the baby girl. Their eyes meet for a long second.

Timidly, almost not daring to, Rebecca reaches out her pale hand and touches the tiny little brown hand of her daughter. It is a gesture that lasts only a second. Rebecca pulls back immediately.

A grimace clouds the remaining beauty of Rebecca's face, as if a shadow has crossed first her mind and then her heart.

EXT. FRONT GATE - MORNING

Maraea busies herself cleaning the leaded glass windows at the main entrance to the Vickers' villa.

In the back garden, hitched to a post next to the white car, Paraiti's mare munches happily from a feed bag hanging by a rope around her neck.

Oti lies between the mare's feet.

Maraea reacts to the sound of a car approaching slowly. Realising that the car has stopped at the entrance to the villa's drive, she rushes to see who is there.

An ELEGANT GENTLEMAN gets out of the car and waves the servant to approach.

Maraea obeys.

> GENTLEMAN
> *Mr Vickers will arrive today. He has sent me with instructions that Mrs Vickers be at the station to meet him.*

The gentleman reaches into his fine suit pocket and produces a telegram that he gives to Maraea. She receives it with her usual lowered gaze.

> GENTLEMAN (CONT'D)
> *I will be here to pick her up at noon.*

> MARAEA
> *Yes, sir. Thank you, sir . . . But I am sure that Mrs Vickers will be quite happy to drive herself to the station.*

Rather taken aback that a servant
would have the impudence to make any
suggestion whatsoever, the gentleman
dismisses her with a wave of his hand.

> GENTLEMAN
> *Give your lady the telegram
> and tell her of Mr Vickers'
> instructions.*

> MARAEA
> *Yes, sir. I will do that, sir.*

The gentleman gets back into the car
and drives off down the street.

Only then Maraea races back to the
house.

INT. REBECCA'S BEDROOM - MORNING

Rebecca lies on her bed, holding the
baby, who is sound asleep in her
embrace.

Seated not far away, Paraiti is
watching them.

Maraea rushes into the room with the
telegram in her hand.

>   MARAEA
>   *You have to leave! Mr Vickers will*
>   *be back today and you cannot be*
>   *here!*

Forbidden to come anywhere near the
baby, Maraea waits in the doorway.

>   MARAEA (CONT'D)
>   *You no longer have any business*
>   *with us.*

Rebecca has been observing both women
in silence and motions that Paraiti
should bring her the telegram.

Paraiti takes the envelope from Maraea
and gives it to Rebecca.

Paraiti leans forward, carefully taking
the child from her mother's arms. She
snuggles the baby to her chest. The
baby whines quietly and Paraiti places
a finger in the child's hungry little
mouth.

Rebecca deliberates a moment before
opening the envelope. Finally, she
reads it, displaying no reaction at
all.

> REBECCA
> (To MARAEA)
> *Prepare my yellow dress. It is his*
> *favorite . . . And yours too . . .*
> *Not a single wrinkle!*

Maraea smiles at her daughter with
genuine relief.

Their old ways are restored. Maraea
quickly leaves the room to fulfil her
mistress's wishes.

Once they are alone again, Paraiti
approaches Rebecca.

> PARAITI
> *You don't need to stay here. Start*
> *your life again . . . You, with*
> *your daughter . . . !*

Rebecca reaches for the baby and
Paraiti replaces the child in her arms.
Rebecca closes her eyes. She pulls the
child to her breast and smiles very
softly.

For the first time, Rebecca and her
daughter are one.

Paraiti steps back and, after a second,
she goes out of the room.

With sad tenderness, Rebecca holds
her baby close to her heart and
whispers to her.

> REBECCA
> *It's all right . . . . It's all*
> *right.*

INT. KITCHEN – DAY

Maraea is at the table. Next to her
lies a cloth nappy and a mountain
of silverware, which she cleans and
polishes with a rag, lemons and the
same white paste she used to bleach
Rebecca's skin.

Preparing to leave the villa for good,
Paraiti enters the room and gathers her
few possessions.

She looks at the servant one last time.

> PARAITI
> *Inaara ko marama koe kai whea te*
> *paihere o tou whakapapa e nehu ana.*
> *Whakanuihia; a tona wa ka murua o*
> *hara e nga atua.*

At least you know where the sacred bond to your lineage is buried. Honour it; maybe one day God will forgive you.

Maraea doesn't stop what she is doing and nor does she raise her eyes.

MARAEA
All I did was provide a better life for my daughter . . . Not the life of a pariah, like me. Not good enough for some, and never pure enough for the others . . . as if I had been a filthy traitor to both sides . . .

Behind them, Rebecca listens quietly from the kitchen doorway. She has the baby in her arms.

MARAEA (CONT'D)
But at least my daughter has a life. She has a house, she has land . . .

Still behind the door and unnoticed by the other women, Rebecca looks down at the peaceful little face of her baby.

MARAEA (CONT'D)
That is much more than what I ever
had . . . Much more than what you
have, Paraiti.

Paraiti turns away from Maraea, ready
to leave, then notices the presence of
Rebecca.

Rebecca approaches Paraiti and,
breaking an embrace that now feels an
integral part of herself, she hands the
baby to her.

Paraiti takes the baby in her arms.

PARAITI
Come with us. Don't stay here.

Rebecca looks at her. Then she draws
with her fingers a line over Paraiti's
scar, just as she did the first time
they met. Only this time it is a caress
filled with gratitude and respect.

Rebecca kisses the baby and turns away
to leave.

Maraea dares to look at her daughter,
not sure how far she can go, and
timidly asks:

> MARAEA
> *Are you going to take your bath*
> *Rebecca?*

Rebecca stops and turns towards Maraea
for the first time since she came down
to the kitchen.

> REBECCA
> *Yes, Mother, I will.*

Maraea smiles at her, but Rebecca is
already gone.

FADE OUT.

FADE IN:

INT. DRESSING ROOM - DAY

Rebecca is wearing a beautiful yellow
silk dress. She just sits, staring at
nothing.

INT. BATHROOM - DAY

Rebecca enters the bathroom.

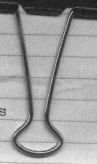

INT. KITCHEN – DAY

Maraea is finishing preparing the
bleaching paste. She places the bowls
on the tray and leaves the kitchen.

INT. CORRIDOR – DAY

With her efficient and precise walk,
Maraea disappears down the end of the
corridor, towards the bathroom.

INT. BATHROOM – DAY

Maraea opens the bathroom door to the
steamy interior.

In the bathtub lies Rebecca. Her body
is under the water, arms at her sides,
the silk of her yellow dress stained by
the blood that flows from her wrists.

Like Sleeping Beauty, she looks
beautiful, silent, peaceful, rested.

LONG FADE TO WHITE.

CREDITS OVER:

<u>EXT. LAKE (EIGHT YEARS
LATER) - MORNING</u>

The same lake where many years before,
at the beginning of our story, Paraiti
was a child.

LITTLE REBECCA, a pretty girl, about
eight years old, with curly ginger-
red hair and brown skin, is sitting on
the ground. She is fully concentrated,
looking at a line of herbs, flowers and
leaves of different shapes and sizes,
which are placed at her feet.

The child's hand takes one of the
flowers and moves it from one place,
and then to another.

After a few seconds, as if coming back
from a place far away, little Rebecca
reacts, she takes the flowers, plants
and herbs from the ground and puts them
inside the old kete that belonged to
Paraiti.

She stands up and runs.

EXT. CAMP BY THE LAKE - MORNING

Older now, Paraiti is outside her camp.

Oti, older as well and as grey as her master, sits by her side.

Little Rebecca runs towards Paraiti and gives her a good squeeze and kiss on the cheek, then sits by her side.

Paraiti smiles at her. She dips a piece of rustic bread in a bowl filled with honey and places it directly in the girl's mouth.

The girl savours her sweet breakfast. Paraiti gives a piece of bread to Oti and then gets one for herself.

The old white horse is not too far away, munching on some grass.

EXT. LAKE - DAY

Paraiti and Rebecca walk by the edge of the lake.

Rebecca picks flowers and herbs, and shows them to Paraiti so she can examine them. Then the little girl puts the flowers inside the old kete, which now hangs from her shoulder.

The horse follows. Farther back, a bit slower, is the dog.

Ahead of them is the magnificent range of mountains.

THE END

NOTES AND ORIGINAL NOVELLA

WITI IHIMAERA

WRITING THE NOVELLAS

1. A SICKLY CHILD

I was my mother Julia's first child. I was premature, a sickly baby with chronic breathing problems. According to her, the Pakeha obstetrician who delivered me didn't think I would live beyond my first year.

This was in the early 1940s, and on her release from Gisborne maternity hospital my mother consulted her doctor, a kindly man named Dr Bowker, and when my breathing problems continued, took me to other Pakeha doctors without telling him. There was a certain amount of desperation about this: she always used to say to me, 'I held you in my arms', as if that explained everything.

My breathing problems continued into my third year. My mother bore a daughter, Kararaina, and then a son, Thomas, who died of a hole in the heart. I think this spurred her to finally turn to her own Maori community of faith healers, including a well-known tohunga, a Ringatu priest known as Hori Gage.

My mother always liked to be formally dressed whenever she went to see important people in the community, so she put on a dark blue suit, stockings, gloves and a hat and drove me to Mangatu, I think it was, where Hori Gage was said to be visiting. However, when she arrived she was told that he had already left to return to his own ancestral lands near Whakatane. She sank to her knees, cradling me in her arms. He had been her final hope.

I know all this because survival narratives are always central to any family, and my mother told them to me to try to instil in me the value of life. Although I was the eldest, compared with my brothers and sisters, I was the sickly runt of the bunch; I still am. And, of course, my mother had already lost Thomas and didn't want to lose another son. I was prone to all the ills and sicknesses of the world, and the stories of my survival were dispensed with all the cod liver oil, malt and other less mentionable concoctions and therapies with which my mother plagued me with as a boy. My siblings did not think of this as special treatment; I made them look good.

Much later, it was intimated to me by another Maori seer that I would not live beyond the age of thirty, which seemed to affirm the doom and gloom with which my early life was surrounded. Of course I am over double that age now, so every year since I have considered a bonus.

My father's approach to my sickliness was much more practical, if wrong. He has always been robust, refusing to believe in mollycoddling and instead favouring fresh air, open windows, cold baths and the like; when I grew older and still had various ailments he liked to threaten me with a health camp. I was therefore putty in his hands when he applied his own remedies to get me well, including one that was popular among Maori in those days: dabbing benzine on a cloth and getting me to inhale it. It's a wonder I didn't turn into a petrolhead.

So there she was, my mother, on her knees in the mud at Mangatu when she felt a gentle tap on her shoulders. 'You should take your son to the medicine woman,' a voice told her.

'My informant was referring to a lady known as Paraiti,' my mother told me, 'or Blightface, because she had a red birthmark over the left half of her cheek running all the way from the hairline to the neck. Like Hori Gage, she was a Ringatu and a follower of the prophet Te Kooti's spiritual ways.'

My mother therefore took this suggestion on its merits and straight away got up, bundled me into my blankets and drove the short way from Mangatu to Whatatutu, where Paraiti was going about her work. Among the stories of babyhood, this was the one that I could imagine fully: stars wheeling above, my anxious white-faced mother speeding down dusty roads looking for a scarred witch doctor, a crying baby in swaddling clothes — you know the sort of thing.

Where was my father? I don't know; he never figured in the narrative.

This must have been around 1946, and the work of such women (and men) was illegal and frowned upon; I understood that Paraiti had been jailed a few times and she practised in a clandestine fashion. When my mother finally found her and delivered me to her for inspection, was Paraiti welcoming? No. First she intimidated my mother with her scar, and then scolded her by saying, 'You should have come straight to me instead of going to Pakeha doctors. Why do you think I will be successful when they haven't been?'

Paraiti must have been in her late seventies by then. She was a girl during the Land Wars and had lived through the flu epidemic of 1918. She had seen many changes as New Zealand became colonised. Grumpy though she was, she looked at me, said she would treat me and, from what Mum told me, for the next week kept me in a makeshift tent filled with herb-infused steam. Every now and then she trickled manuka honey down my throat.

'Some days later,' my mother told me, 'Paraiti began to karakia, to pray, and, as she did so, she hooked a finger into your throat and pulled out threads of phlegm.'

2. HONOURING PARAITI

It is from this childhood survival story that I wrote *White Lies,* which was originally published as *Medicine Woman* in my 2007 collection, *Ask the Posts of the House.* In fact I had toyed with calling that collection 'Medicine Woman', but, at the last moment, chose the other title because it appeared to have more potency and gravitas.

Now comes the film directed by Mexican director Dana Rotberg. It will be the third feature film to be made from my work after *Whale Rider* in 2002 and *Nights in the Gardens of Spain* in 2010. (Known as *Kawa* for its American release in 2011, the latter film won a prestigious National Geographic indigenous award and was released in Germany with subtitles in 2012.) In both the novella of *Medicine Woman* and film of *White Lies* the name of Paraiti has been kept for the main character.

And, of course, there is a sequence in the film in which a young boy has manuka honey trickled down his throat so that he can breathe.

I have tried to recreate Paraiti's late nineteenth- and early to mid-twentieth-century world in the first half of the narrative, which follows her travels with horse, mule and dog throughout the wilderness tribal lands of my childhood. Most New Zealanders will know the historical context that I refer to, involving the prophet Te Kooti Arikirangi and his followers — the Ringatu. Surely the settler country feared Te Kooti. During the early days of the Land Wars between the two races, they had wrongly imprisoned him, in

1866, on the Chatham Islands, seven days' sail from New Zealand. He was incarcerated for two long years, but during his time there the spirit of God visited him and inspired him to create a religion, the Ringatu, and to lead the Maori people out of bondage, just as Moses had done when he defied Pharaoh and led the Israelites out of Egypt. Te Kooti and his fledgling followers escaped from the Chathams by boat, and when they landed back in Aotearoa the Pakeha militia pursued them relentlessly. In retaliation, in November 1868, Te Kooti led an attack on the military garrison at Matawhero. It was an act of war and from then on the prophet and his followers were marked; a ransom was placed on Te Kooti's head. For ten years he evaded capture, moving swiftly from one kainga to another, always supported by his followers.

White Lies begins during these years. In it I have tried to document the world of the itinerant Maori healer, piecing it together from my own childhood experiences, local Ringatu and other informants and the scarce mentions in historic documents and other sources. My thanks to my dear mentor Maaka Jones — herself a Ringatu tohunga and versed in Maori medicine — and family and local Waituhi informants for oral stories about Paraiti and medicine women of her kind. My father, Te Haa o Ruhia, was the one who told me about traditional Maori massage and how his shoulder was set right simply by massaging the bones together; the account of Paraiti massaging her father with her loving hands at his death also comes from him. Thanks to the authors of the following books: Judith Binney's *Redemption Songs: A Life of Te Kooti Arikirangi Te Turuki* (Auckland University Press, 1995); Murdoch Riley and Brian Enting's indispensable *Maori Healing and Herbal Medicines* (Viking Sevenseas, 1994); and Roger Neich's *Painted Histories: Early Maori Figurative Painting* (Auckland University Press, 1993). Any errors of fact are mine. I am not an expert on the Ringatu or, particularly, on traditional healing and medicine, and I apologise for any inaccuracies. Thanks also to the Manukau Institute of Technology, the Arts Foundation of New Zealand and Creative New Zealand for research and funding assistance during the period I wrote the novella printed in this edition.

3. MERLE OBERON WAS A MAORI

However, when I was writing the novella I realised that the fictional Paraiti needed a moral dilemma, something that would challenge her purpose and her thinking: a confrontation with all that she values and believes.

In the second part of her story, therefore, I introduced a character named Rebecca Vickers, a young Pakeha society woman in her twenties, who asks Paraiti for an abortion. But Mrs Vickers and her maidservant, Maraea, in her fifties and a Maori, are not what they seem to be. In particular, Mrs Vickers has a lot at stake: if the baby is born, and if it is of dark complexion, people will realise that she is Maori.

This is where I have interpolated the story of actress Merle Oberon. It provides the heart of darkness for *Medicine Woman* and *White Lies*.

I have been fascinated by Merle Oberon ever since reading *Merle: A Biography of Merle Oberon* by Charles Higham and Roy Moseley (New English Library, 1983). All her life she lived a lie. She told the press that she had been born in Hobart, Tasmania. In 1965, she found herself in Sydney when she accompanied her then husband Bruno Pagliai, one of the richest men in Latin America, on an inaugural Aeronaves de Mexico flight to Australia. Invited to attend a banquet in her honour at Government House in Hobart, she first accepted, then fainted and cancelled; she was in Australia for only seventy-two hours.

Why the deception? Well, Merle Oberon had a lot to hide. She was, after all, one of the most beautiful women of her generation, a famous film actress with a fabulous almond-shaped face and slanting eyes set in a flawlesss white complexion. In a film career that lasted from 1930 to 1973, her electrifying beauty was highlighted in over fifty British, French, American and Mexican films, including playing Anne Boleyn to Charles Laughton in *The Private Life of Henry VIII* (1933), Cathy to Laurence Olivier's Heathcliff in *Wuthering Heights* (1939), George Sand to Cornel Wilde's Chopin in *A Song to Remember* (1945) and the Empress Josephine to Marlon Brando's Napoleon in *Desirée* (1954). People thought she had discovered the fountain of youth because as she grew older she seemed to become more beautiful.

Merle Oberon achieved much more than a film career. In a life characterised by steely determination, sexual charisma and force of will, she moved in the international jet set, becoming one of the leading hostesses for her multi-millionaire husband, lavishly entertaining princes and presidents at their sumptuous home in Mexico. Higham and Moseley are of the view that she dominated not only Hollywood but the society of her generation.

All this, and yet she was the second daughter of a Eurasian girl, born on 19 February 1911 not in Tasmania, Australia, but in Bombay, India.

This was the description of Merle Oberon's mother in Higham and Moseley's book that took my attention: 'Her name is Charlotte Constance Selby . . . She is a Christian girl, part Irish, part Singhalese, with Maori strains in her blood . . .' The future actress was christened Estelle Merle. Her father was Arthur O'Brien Thompson, and the name Merle Oberon was fashioned out of her second Christian name and her father's first surname.

When Merle Oberon became famous, her mother, father and her elder sister conspired to keep the truth of her Eurasian origins from the public. According to Higham and Moseley, cinematographers found ways of filming her so that her naturally dark skin and looks would be obscured. One such was the famed Gregg Toland, cameraman for *Citizen Kane*, who poured the whitest and most blazing arc lights directly into her face, making her look almost transparently fair and removing any hint of her Indian skin texture.

Merle Oberon's mother, Charlotte, in fact lived with her daughter in Britain and the United States, and the biography relates this incident from the 1930s, told by actress Diana Napier (p. 28): 'One afternoon I was having tea with Merle at her flat near Baker Street when for the first time I saw this little, plump Indian woman come into the room dressed in a sari. She stood nervous, hesitantly, as though waiting for orders. Merle was extremely embarrassed. She spoke to her mother in Hindustani. The lady hardly said anything at all. She was very, very quiet.'

Charlotte Constance Selby died with her daughter at her bedside on 28 April 1937. Very few people knew that the Indian woman, called by Merle Oberon her ayah or nanny, had been her mother. Neither woman had ever shown any sign of family affection. To have done so would have destroyed Merle Oberon's 'English rose' reputation at a time when women of colour faced harrowing prejudice and racism. In the British film industry, such a woman would never have made it to the front rank of actors — and would not have survived the furore if the truth had become known.

Soon after her mother's death, so Higham and Moseley tell us, Merle Oberon had a portrait painted of an unknown woman, with brown hair, blue eyes and white skin, dressed in a period costume of some twenty years earlier. The painting always hung in her homes from then on, and, when asked who the woman was, Merle Oberon always said she was her mother.

And so, in the second part of the novella and film, Paraiti

is involved in a battle of wills with Rebecca Vickers, whose life parallels that of Merle Oberon: as a Maori passing as Pakeha, she, too, has much at stake.

The battle is over the life of an unborn child: how will Paraiti be able to save the child and not kill it? It is also, of course, over whose history will succeed, identity, race, skin colour and the choices many men and women of ethnicity faced when trying to survive within European society before it rebalanced itself.

4. AN EVOLVING STORY

There are now two versions of the novella *Medicine Woman*, which, together with the *White Lies* screenplay, make three versions of the same story. The following first version of the novella was first published in *Ask the Posts of the House* (2007), and this is the version on which Dana Rotberg based her *White Lies* adaptation. The second, expanded and altered version, is published for the first time at the beginning of this movie tie-in.

Those who know my work will understand why: I have a habit of rewriting; for instance, there are two versions of *Pounamu, Pounamu* (1972 and 2002), two versions of *Tangi* (1973 and the second substantially revised combined with a sequel called *The Rope of Man*, 2005), two versions of *Whanau* (*Whanau* 1974 and *Whanau II*, 2003), two versions of *The Matriarch* (1986 and its major revision 2009), retouching of various versions of *The Whale Rider* and multiple published versions of some of my short stories.

My last novel, *The Parihaka Woman* (2011), actually began life as *Erenora*, an unpublished rock opera libretto, before becoming a novella originally intended for inclusion in *The Thrill of Falling*, but it grew into a complete novel instead.

The reason?

Well, I have always believed that a fictional piece of work exists in a continuum. It is not static. Stories rarely leave you alone, they sit like backseat drivers in the recesses of your mind, nagging to come back into the driving seat again. Indeed, my publisher Harriet Allan said to me, 'Witi, you must have a busload of bossy characters at the back of *your* bus!' There's more: they also nag at me, 'Pay further attention to who we really are and the landscape that you are driving us through.' And so in most cases I have added historical context or political inflections or sub-textual resonances.

In the case of *Medicine Woman* there was another reason. This was that from the beginning the novella was always the first part of a two-part story: *Medicine Woman* and *Paraiti's Daughter*. I still have to write the sequel, but its rewrite was evolving in my head at the same time Dana was writing her screenplay adaptation. I like to think that it is a more complex work, and certainly it provides a richer and more substantial — and longer — experience for the reader.

I'm not going to point out the differences between my original *Medicine Woman* and this current rendition — they will be apparent when you read them — except to say that two characters have a greater part to play in the expanded version: Ihaka the woodsman and the anonymous gardener; this is because they serve a larger function in the sequel. They were also demanding their own stories in the future. My editor Anna Rogers and Harriet, too, also required me with their excellent questions to audit the original and add detail that they felt was missing in it. All this was done without recourse to Dana's screenplay.

I should also point out that there are now three variations on the ending. In the original novella in *Ask the Posts of the House,* it is Rebecca Vickers who throws the baby into the river. However, in Dana's *White Lies* screenplay, Rebecca commits suicide, which caused me a dilemma as far as writing any sequel was concerned. This is why I was pushed to make Maraea, and not Rebecca Vickers, the one who takes the baby down to the bridge before sunrise. As it happens, this change has brought Maraea out of the shadows, makes us focus on her motivations — and prepares us for her greater participation in the sequel.

I like to think that the reader and viewer of Dana's film now have the opportunity to choose which ending they prefer. For fledgling writers and filmmakers, the three endings show the different direction ideas can be taken by different artists, filmmakers, publishers and editors working in different media.

They show that the capacity of the artistic imagination is limitless.

Thanks to my friend and colleague John Barnett, whose production company made *Whale Rider* and who introduced Dana Rotberg to me. Most people won't know that it took twelve years to bring *Whale Rider,* directed by Niki Caro, from novel to screen. John introduced me to Niki, too; she is one of my favourite people. The most successful New Zealand stories that appear on film and television in this country are due to his tenacity; I am humbled and grateful that South Pacific Pictures have produced *White Lies — Tuakiri Huna.*

Thank you also to Dana Rotberg. What an amazing biography she brings to New Zealand: an acclaimed director in Mexico, with a list of international award-winning films to her credit! After a decade-long hiatus, *White Lies—Tuakiri Huna* marks her return to international filmmaking. From the beginning, I was excited at the prospect of such an acclaimed filmmaker bringing her aesthetic and vision to a New Zealand landscape and narrative; we have usually been seen only through New Zealand or British or American eyes. *White Lies—Tuakiri Huna* is clearly the work of a major international director; Dana Rotberg's notes, written with sincerity and radiance, show why.

As well, I could not help but feel some strange rightness in the Mexican connection through Merle Oberon's marriage to Bruno Pagliai.

In her acknowledgements, Dana thanks the many people from Tuhoe, the Ruatahuna valley and those involved in the production for the making of *White Lies—Tuakiri Huna*. May I add my thanks that you so fulsomely and generously opened the pathway for her, and the cast and crew.

Thanks also to my agent, Ray Richards, and to my publisher Harriet Allan and my editor Anna Rogers for their superb advice and editing; they never let me get away with anything.

Finally, I want to return to my mother and the scar-faced woman she took me to. She was a woman I never knew called Paraiti.

During the making of the film, John Barnett told the story of Paraiti at the blessing at the marae before production began. I was so proud to know that filming was to take place on the Oputao Marae and I make my mihi and pay tribute to the kuia, koroua and whanau for their generosity and aroha. I was not there, but apparently the local people were intrigued about my story. They were aware of local women who practised medicine but not one of them could identify the real Paraiti.

Does that matter? Yes, because one day I would like to visit her grave, wherever it might be, and thank her for her work.

Anointed to the task of honouring life, she saved mine.

Witi Ihimaera
Auckland

MEDICINE WOMAN

THE ORIGINAL
NOVELLA BY
WITI IHIMAERA

1

Another dawn, and she drags her old bones up from sleep.

Her name is Paraiti and when she is sleeping her bones are light and weightless. But as she wakes she is aware of all the stiffness, aches and numbness of a body that has aged. She opens her eyes, listening to her heart thumping away as it pushes the blood through thickened veins. She hears the usual wheeze and gurgle as her lungs force her breath in and out, and she feels a lump of phlegm in her throat. Creaking like an old door on worn-out hinges, she heaves herself into a sitting position, opens the flap of the tent and spits into the cuspidor she keeps for holding her offensive bodily fluids.

Now that she is awake, Paraiti fumbles among her blankets for her Bible and hymnal and starts to chant a karakia. Old habits die hard, and she wouldn't dream of beginning a new day without himene and prayer. Her parents Te Teira and Hera, if they were alive, would roar with laughter to see her now; in the old days, when the Ringatu faithful were all at prayer in the smoky meeting house, she was the child always squirming and wriggling. 'Kaore e korikori koe,' Te Teira would reprimand her.

Although Paraiti went for a few years to a native school, she can't read very well; she trusts to her memory when quoting from the Old

Testament or singing hymns. She raises a hand in the sign of the faithful.

'Kororia ki to ingoa tapu,' she begins. 'Glory be to Thy holy name.'

She lifts her eyes to the sky lightening above her, and gives thanks to God for having made the world. The huge forest canopy has been a protective umbrella for her sleep. Here, at the bend of a river, with giant ferns unfolding in the lower growth, she has had the perfect camping ground.

Karakia over, she whistles out to her stallion, Ataahua, and Kaihe, her mule. They whinny back — good, they have not foraged too far away in the night. Where's Tiaki, her pig dog? Aha, there he is, on the other side of the river.

She calls to him, 'Have you brought something for my breakfast or have you been selfish and wolfed it all down yourself?'

No, today Tiaki has been kind to his mistress. He jumps headlong into the water and swims across; he offers a fat wood pigeon, still alive and unmarked in his jaws.

'Homai te kereru,' Paraiti asks him. 'Give me the bird.' He sighs, knowing she will release it back into the woods. 'Ae, Tiaki, we let this one go. Give the first to Tane, Lord of the Forest.' She gives the pigeon its freedom and it creaks and whistles its way back into the trees. 'Now go, Tiaki, the second pigeon is for us.'

Right-oh, down to the edge of the river to wash herself, get the pikaro out of her eyes, and use a clean rag to wash her neck, armpits and nether parts. While she is at it, she sprinkles water over her head, and looks at her reflection, hoping to see some improvement. No such luck. Still the same old face, only getting older: big Maori nose, heavy upper lip, three chins, and lots of bushy hair. She fixes the hair by pinning it back with two large ivory combs but, aue, now she can see more of her face. Never mind: there's nobody else around to frighten.

Time for breakfast. Paraiti rekindles the fire and hangs a billy of water on an iron rod supported by two strong branches; she also puts a skillet among the hot embers.

Tiaki comes back with a second bird. Paraiti has a sneaking suspicion that he catches two birds at the same time and, somehow, has learnt the trick of pinning the second bird down with a stone, keeping it for later. Now that he has served his mistress, Tiaki bounds off in search of his own breakfast.

Paraiti plucks the pigeon and puts it in the skillet; very soon it is sizzling in its own fat. From one of her saddlebags she takes some damper bread and honey. There's nothing like a fresh pigeon and damper bread running with honey to start the day. A cup of manuka tea made in the billy and, ka pai, she is in seventh heaven.

Once she's breakfasted, she's keen to get going. Quickly, she dismantles the tent and bedding and stows them in the saddlebag. She goes down to the river to rinse the breakfast implements, then douses the fire and cleans up around her. She buries the contents of the cuspidor in the ground. Nobody would ever know she'd been here.

At Paraiti's whistle, Ataahua and Kaihe come at the gallop. She loads Kaihe first, then she puts the bridle and saddle on Ataahua and taps him on the front knees. Once upon a time she could get on a horse without trouble, but these days it's too much for her old bones. Ataahua obliges, going down on his front legs. He waits for Paraiti to settle and then hoists himself up with a whinny of grumpiness; over the past few years his mistress has got not only older but heavier.

'Me haere tatou,' she tells Ataahua. 'Let us go.'

Pulling her mule after her, she fords the river and climbs the track on the other side. By the time she reaches the top of the ridge, Tiaki has joined her with a supercilious look on his face, as if he has given her only the second-best pigeon. The mist has lifted from the valleys and the air is clear. The forest is raucous with birdsong. Far away, Paraiti can see the smoke curling above the village of Ruatahuna, her destination.

2

Paraiti is not her real name, but the name people know her by. Mostly she is called Scarface — emblematic of the deep red welt that travels diagonally from her right temple across the bridge of her nose and, luckily missing her left eye, reappears to feather her left cheekbone. The scar was caused when Paraiti was a young girl, in 1880. Her family group was hiding deep within the Urewera country when they were set upon by constabulary forces who were hunting bigger game — the rebel prophet, Te Kooti. They restrained Paraiti's parents with ropes while they ransacked the encampment. When they couldn't find Te Kooti, one of them took a burning stick from the cooking fire and slashed Paraiti with it. As her parents were led away to be imprisoned, her father Te Teira cried out, 'Daughter, quickly, go to the stream and lie down in the cold water.' Hera, Paraiti's mother, died while they were still incarcerated, and when Te Teira was released a year later, he went searching throughout Tuhoe and the King Country for his daughter. As soon as he saw the scarred little girl on the roadside at Te Kuiti, where she had been lovingly cared for, he knew it was her.

●

Today is the first day of June in the Year of Our Lord, nineteen hundred and twenty-nine. Paraiti is fifty-four years old now, and a traditional healer.

Maori people have not lost faith in their own healers. Indeed, although those who live in the cities and towns have access to the Pakeha doctors, those who still reside in tribal villages in the backblocks and remote coastal areas rely on travelling healers like Paraiti for medical help. Vilified by the government authorities for their work, the healers are still committed to the health and wellbeing of the morehu, the survivors of the land wars. Many of Paraiti's people of the Ringatu faith do not trust the authorities at all. And, of course, the Depression is beginning to bite. Who can Maori turn to, apart from their own healers, when they have no money to pay the Pakeha takuta?

Three weeks ago, Paraiti was still in her village of Waituhi, preparing for her travels. The autumn had been unseasonably cold, with southerlies driving into the foothills. Paraiti had huddled close to a warm fire in her old one-room kauta near the painted meeting house, Rongopai. Even so, she was determined to keep to her annual trip. She had become stir-crazy and wanted to be out on the road.

It was time for her to leave her hearth.

She carefully selected the medicines, unguents, potions, analgesics, antiseptics, styptics, philtres, emetics, blood purifiers and ointments that she needed. She took only kao, dried kumara and water as provisions; food would be her payment from her patients and, should she require extra kai for herself and her animals, the Lord and the land provided. She knew all the traditional food-gathering areas — fern grounds, pa tuna, taro and kumara gardens and bird sanctuaries — and, as well, she had some special secret areas where she went to stock up on herbs and healing plants.

Paraiti took a small tent and a bedroll. For protection she put her rifle in a sling and a knife in her left boot. Although she might not be attractive, she was still a woman, and men were men.

She went to Rongopai, the great cathedral of her people, and in its stunning interior — verily a Garden of Eden — she prayed to God for safe passage. She filled five blue bottles with the healing waters that bubbled up from a deep underground spring behind the house, and sprinkled herself and her animals with the water. Then she strapped the saddlebags around Kaihe's girth, bridled and saddled Ataahua, tapped on his front knees and climbed aboard. Straightaway, she urged Ataahua up, 'Timata,' and headed into the foothills behind Waituhi.

A day's travel took her to the boundary between the lands of Te Whanau a Kai and Tuhoe, and there she sought Rua's Track, one of the great horse tracks joining the central North Island to the tribes of Poverty Bay in the east. She followed the track up the Wharekopae River, through Waimaha by way of the Hangaroa Valley to Maungapohatu. The only people who travelled the track were Maori like herself; sometimes they were families but most often they were foresters, labourers or pig hunters.

On her third day, however, Paraiti joined a wagon-train of some forty members; they, too, were making for Ruatahuna. They knew who she was and were honoured to have her join them. And she, in turn, valued the opportunity to sharpen up her social skills, to share a billy of manuka tea and flat bread, to spend time playing cards and to korero with some of the old ones about the way the world was changing. But they made slow progress, so Paraiti took her leave of them and journeyed on alone.

And now, Ruatahuna lay ahead.

●

As she approaches Ruatahuna, Paraiti knows she will be late for the service. She can hear the bell ringing at the meeting house, Te Whai a Te Motu, calling the Ringatu faithful to gather together on this very special day. The First of June in the church calendar is the Sabbath of the Sabbath, as written in Leviticus 23:4: 'Ko nga hakari nunui enei a Ihowa, ko nga huihuinga tapu e karangatia e koutou i nga wa e rite ai.' It is also the beginning of the Maori New Year, with the pre-dawn heliacal rising of Matariki, the bright stars of fruitfulness. On this happy day, each person contributes seeds to the mara tapu, the sacred garden. This is part of the huamata ritual, for out of the old seed comes the new plant, symbolic of the renewal of God's promise to all his people.

Paraiti urges Ataahua quickly through the village. Some of the local dogs bark at them, and Paraiti gives Tiaki a warning glance, 'Don't bark back, it's Sunday.' He gives her a sniffy look, then growls menacingly at the dogs so that they whine and back away. Ahead, Paraiti sees her cousin Horiana's house. She knows Horiana won't mind if she ties the animals to her fence. 'Don't eat Horiana's roses,' she tells Kaihe. Even so, she is troubled to see that the roses are taking over the native vines in the garden.

Wrapping her scarf around her face, and taking with her a small sachet of seeds, Paraiti makes for the marae. Horses and buggies are tied to the fence outside and, hello, a few motoka as well. Inside, the meeting house is stacked to the gills; people are sitting up against the walls, prayer books in hand. Wirepa, the local poutikanga, pillar of authority, is leading the service.

'Kororia ki to ingoa tapu,' he intones. 'And verily, an angel appeared to the prophet Te Kooti, and the angel was clothed in garments as white as snow, his hair like stars, and he wore a crown and a girdle like unto the setting sun and the rising thereof, and the angel's fan was like the rainbow and his staff was a myriad hues. And the angel said to Te Kooti, "I will not forsake thee or my people either." And so we prevail to this very day. Glory be to thy holy name. Amine.'

Paraiti sees Horiana beckoning and making a place beside her. Stooping, she makes her way over to her cousin.

'E noho, whanaunga,' Horiana welcomes her. They kiss and hug as if they haven't seen each other for a thousand years. 'We'll korero afterwards,' Horiana whispers, opening her prayer book.

Paraiti gives a sign of apology to Wirepa for interrupting the

service. She hears a buzz as people realise she has arrived: 'Scarface
. . . Te Takuta . . . Paraiti . . . Scarface.' She smiles at familiar faces.
She doesn't mind that people call her Scarface; they use the name as
an identification, not to mock her. She lets herself be absorbed into
the meeting house. It is such an honour to be sitting within Te Whai a
Te Motu, with its figurative paintings and beautiful kowhaiwhai rafter
patterns. Here, in the bosom of this holy place, Paraiti joins in praising
and giving thanks to God.

The service adjourns to the mara tapu outside Te Whai a Te Motu.
There, Paraiti and others offer their seeds for the sowing. Wirepa
intones a final karakia. After the service there are people to be greeted
and further korero to be had with the local elders.

After the midday meal, Paraiti sets up her tent in her usual place
on the marae. Horiana, who acts as her assistant in Tuhoe, has been
taking bookings. 'Lots of people want to see you,' she tells her. 'The
usual problems. Nothing too difficult so far.' Always bossy, Horiana
sits outside the tent deciding when clients should enter and depart.
Inside, there are three chairs and a bed: a slab of wood covered with a
fine woven flax mat. Stacked against one of the walls of the tent are the
rongoa and the herbal pharmacy that Paraiti draws on for her work. Not
all have been brought by her; some have been stockpiled by Horiana for
her arrival. They include kumarahou for asthma; waoriki for arthritis;
ake, kareao, miro or rimu gum for bleeding and haemorrhaging;
hakekakeha or harakeke roots for blood cleansing and to promote
regular blood functions; mingimingi, the mamaku pith and punga
fern pith for scrofulous tumours, abcesses and boils; kawakawa for
bronchitis and catarrh; weka oil, kowhai and bluegum juice for bruises,
sprains and aching bones; harakeke and kauri gum to treat burns;
puwha and mimiha gum for mouth and teeth ailments; harakeke for
chilblains and bad circulation; houhere and tawa for colds; titoki for
constipation; piupiu for cramp; wood charcoal for dandruff; koromiko
buds for diarrhoea and dysentery; eel oil for earache; powdered moss
for eczema and scabies; kaikaiatua as an emetic; pirita for epilepsy;

seaweed for goitre; paewhenua for haemorrhoids; piripiri for urinary health; fernroot and convolvulus roots for lactation; flax leaf juice for sciatica; huainanga as an emetic to expel tapeworms and so on.

On a small table are the surgical implements of her trade. Unlike some of her brother and sister healers, Paraiti shuns Pakeha utensils and keeps to traditional ones: wooden sticks and scrapers, sharp-edged shells and obsidian flakes for cutting, thorns for opening up abscesses, stones to heat before placing on the body, lacy houhere bark and cobwebs as poultices and dressings, palm tree splints for broken bones, kahakaha fibre for bandaging, and various oils for massaging.

For any major bonesetting that requires steam treatment, Paraiti organises times at a makeshift spa. Her father gave her special knowledge of the various massages to heal and knit broken bones. He also taught her therapeutic massage for the elderly; he himself loved nothing better than to submit himself to Paraiti's strong kneading and stroking of his body to keep his circulation going. 'Daughter,' he would sigh, 'you have such goodness in your hands.'

The clinic opens, and the patients are of the usual kind. Some are easily treated — patients with coughs or colds and children with asthma or bronchitis. Boils are lanced and the ripe cores squeezed out before Paraiti returns the patient to Horiana to apply a poultice. Paraiti gives a short greeting to patients returning for a check-up, and notes whether a broken leg has set well, or a burn is in need of further bathing or lotions. Sprained joints, too, are treated with ease; with Horiana holding the patient, Paraiti pulls the joint back in place, then instructs Horiana how to bind it.

A young man with a deep cut on his forehead comes in. 'How did you come by this?' Paraiti asks.

'His wife threw a knife at him when he came home drunk from the hotel,' Horiana answers, rolling her eyes with contempt.

'You will need stitches,' Paraiti says. She makes a thread of muka and uses a wooden needle to sew the wound. As a dressing, she applies the ash from a burnt flax stalk. Throughout all this, the young man does not flinch. He's a cheeky one, though; just before he leaves he asks, 'Scarface, you couldn't throw in a love philtre with the treatment, could you? My wife's still angry with me and won't let me perform my customary and expert lovemaking duties.'

Paraiti's eyes twinkle. 'Oh really? But I have heard otherwise about your lovemaking. Do you think it might be the beer that is putting you off your stroke? No love philtre is required. Your wife will eventually forgive you and soon you will plough her in your usual diligent and boring manner, the poor woman. But if you must drink, chew puwha gum — it will mask your breath when you go home at night.'

Another young man comes in, but, as soon as he sees Paraiti, he changes his mind and goes out. He is embarrassed because he has a venereal disease. A male takuta is preferred to a woman healer.

A young woman with shell splinters in the heels of her feet requires a little more care; she carelessly ran across a reef while gathering pupu and mussels. 'I was being chased by a giant octopus,' she tells Paraiti.

Paraiti winks at Horiana. 'Oh yes, and what was his name?' She cuts around the wounds until the pieces of shell can be seen. Smiling at the young woman, Paraiti then lowers her head. 'Here is the kiss of Scarface,' she says. She bites on each piece of shell with her teeth and pulls them out. 'If your octopus really loves you and wants to ensnare you in his eight arms, and if that causes you to run over shells again, show him how to use his own teeth.'

The next patient causes some hilarity. He has constipation and hasn't had a good bowel movement for days. 'I have just the right potion,' Paraiti tells him. 'Crushed flax roots and, here, if you disrobe, I will also blow some potion into your rectum so that the result comes quicker.' But the patient's wife is with him and she accosts Paraiti:

'Oh no, you don't! If anybody is to disrobe my husband and blow anything up his rectum, it will be me! Do I want the whole world to know how awful a sight his bum is? Best for him and me to keep that treasure a family secret.'

So it goes on throughout the remainder of the day; each patient pays Paraiti in coin or in food — a koha, no matter how small.

However, there are some who are sick without obvious symptoms and their treatment cannot be diagnosed with ease. With such patients Paraiti takes a history of their activities before they became ill and, if she suspects an answer, administers a likely remedy. If she is still unsure, she advises the patient to drink lots of clean water and gives them a potion against the pain or fever. 'Sometimes,' she tells them, 'the body has its own ways of making itself well again. Time will tell.'

There are other patients whom Paraiti will treat separately, away from the clinic at Horiana's house, because their conditions are more serious. One is a forester with a broken leg that will need to be broken again; Paraiti believes his best recourse would be to go to the hospital at Rotorua but the forester refuses to let their doctors look at him — he is worried about the expense. Another is a young girl with an eye condition that bespeaks oncoming blindness. A third is an old koroua with a debilitating illness; nothing can cure old age but, as she often did with her father, Paraiti will give this old man a good massage and steam bath for temporary relief. He is already walking towards God.

The time comes to stop work for the day. 'Come back tomorrow,' Horiana tells the other people waiting in line. They are disappointed, but another day won't hurt them.

'But I will see the mother,' Paraiti says, pointing to a woman waiting with her daughter. She has constantly given up her place in the line to others.

'Thank you, takuta,' the mother says respectfully as she steps into the tent. She is trying to hide her distress. 'Actually, I do not come for my own sake but on behalf of my daughter, Florence. Do you have something that will enable her to keep her baby? She can never go to term and loses the baby always around the third month.'

Paraiti notices how small Florence is. She places her hands on the girl's stomach. E hika, this girl is very cold.

'How many times have you conceived?' Paraiti asks her.

'Three,' Florence replies, 'and three times my babies have died inside me. But I really want this child.'

Paraiti takes a look at the girl. She smells her breath; aue, she smokes the Pakeha cigarettes. She looks at her eyes; they are milky and clouded, and her fingernails and toenails are brittle and dry. Finally, Paraiti feels with her fingers around the girl's womb — again, so cold. She speaks, not unkindly, to the girl.

'A baby in the womb is like a kumara being fed nutrients from the vine of your body. But your vine is not giving your baby the right foods. Your circulation is sluggish and, therefore, the nourishment is not getting to the child. Bad foods and bad vine are the reasons why, in the third month, your baby withers and dies. Also, the garden in which your baby grows is not warm.'

Paraiti looks at Florence's mother. 'I will put your daughter on a diet, which she must follow without straying,' she tells her. 'The diet is rich in nutrients. I will also put her on a regime of exercise that will improve her circulation. Florence must stop smoking Pakeha cigarettes immediately. Also, it is important that her blood temperature is increased. I will show you massages to make her body a whare tangata that is nice and cosy. Keep to the diet, the massages, and make sure she stays in the sunlight and eats vegetables and fruits and fish, especially shellfish. Try to make sure she is always warm.'

The mother holds Paraiti's hands and kisses them. 'Thank you, takuta.'

Paraiti sees them to the door of the tent. 'I will also give you some potions that will improve Florence's health while she is with child.'

'Will you attend the birth?' the mother asks.

'No,' Paraiti answers. 'The authorities will not allow it.' She turns to Florence. 'Go well, and be assured that if you follow my instructions, the birth should be normal and you will be delivered of a healthy child.' She kisses Florence on the forehead. 'What greater blessing can any woman have than to give birth to a son or daughter for the iwi? Will you let me know when the baby is born? Ma te Atua koe e manaaki.'

3

This is Paraiti's life and world. She is an agent of life, prolonging and optimising it. Paraiti's knowledge, therefore, is of the treatment of the body not the spirit, though sometimes these two are intertwined.

But Paraiti does not live and practise at the higher level of a tohunga. She is not a mediator between the human world and the spiritual world. She does not heal mate atua, diseases of the gods; she has no competency in dealing with those sicknesses that are due to possession of the spirit. While she has known some very great priests — with skills in the spiritual, arcane and esoteric arts: prophecy, dream, sign, rehu, whakakitenga, makutu, moemoea and whiu — that is not her domain. Nor does she return spells onto those responsible for casting them.

Paraiti's father was such a priest, a man of immense wisdom, whom the iwi consulted on all matters of importance because of his powers of divination. Indeed, it was as a priest that Te Teira had served the great prophet Te Kooti, and remained loyal to him to the very end; this was why the people of Te Kuiti had looked after Paraiti, and had taken them both in after he was released from prison. Te Teira loved to talk about the early days of the prophet's victories. He used the language of the Old Testament, and likened Te Kooti's exploits to the great exodus and the flight of the Israelites from the lands of Egypt into the Canaan. It was all metaphorical talk but Paraiti was moved by its grandeur and imagery. 'In the end Te Kooti was pardoned,' Te Teira told Paraiti as they sat in front of the fire in their kauta. 'I will tell you how. The government wanted to run a railway line through the King country, and issued a general amnesty to all criminals, no matter what they had done, to secure the land. The prophet was saved by the iron horse!' he laughed.

'It was 1884 when that railway opened,' he went on. 'You and I were travelling to some hui or other, I can't remember which one, but you were my right-hand man, do you remember? We came across some Ringatu boys bending over the rails listening. We got off our horses too and bent down and listened. And your eyes went big and wide and you said to me, "Papa, the rails are singing a strange waiata!" Then suddenly, around the corner came that iron horse, a huge ngarara, a monster, belching smoke and roaring at us. Our horses started to buck and bolt but, resolute in the face of the ngarara, you raised your rifle and fired a shot at it.' Te Teira laughed. 'I suppose you were still trying to protect your papa, ne?'

Paraiti's shot did not bring the ngarara to the ground. But as it swayed and slithered past, she saw the many men and women who had been eaten by it, imprisoned in its intestines. She raised a tangi to them, a great lament. Of course, she had been mistaken. The passengers in the train were very much alive, dispersing into settlements — and the ngarara was just another monster eating up the land.

It was in Te Kuiti that Paraiti grew into womanhood. Although Te Teira would have wished for her to marry some kind farmer or fisherman of the tribe, raise children and live a happy life, those options were closed to her because of her kanohi wera, her burnt face. No matter that he was revered for his medical skills; even his great mana could not obtain a husband for her. She was twenty-four and already accustomed to rejection when, in a terrible moment of truth, she asked, 'Father, what man, in the moment of ecstasy, would look upon my face and not wish it was someone else's?' Te Teira himself acknowledged that his daughter was destined to become a spinster, with no provider once he was gone.

Paraiti's father had to go underground when the Tohunga Suppression Act was passed in 1908. The purpose of the Act was to replace tohunga, traditional Maori healers, with 'modern medicine'. The politicians made a lot of noise about 'charlatan' tohunga, but the Act was primarily directed at Rua Kenana who, some say, succeeded Te Kooti as prophet. 'As when the Pakeha pardoned Te Kooti,' Te Teira said, 'they brought in a law ostensibly for one thing when it was really for another.'

Te Teira had defied the Act by continuing to practise covertly. And he taught his daughter the arts of healing so that she could achieve economic independence as a functioning member of the iwi. In 1917, when Paraiti was forty-two, the Spanish influenza hit Maori settlements and the people were unable to get treatment from the Pakeha doctors. Paraiti joined her father in offering succour and support to the sick and dying in Te Kuiti. The irony was that the disease had been brought among the people by the Maori soldiers who had gone to fight in the Great War, on the other side of the world.

After the epidemic was over, Te Teira received a letter from a powerful kuia of Te Whanau a Kai on the East Coast, asking him to come and help her in improving the health of her people. Her name was Riripeti, and her persuasive powers were so great that, eventually, with the consent of the people of Te Kuiti, Te Teira accepted her offer. He migrated east with his daughter and they ended up in Waituhi. There Te Teira finished installing in Paraiti the safer knowledge — not the knowledge of the tohunga, but the knowledge of the healer. In particular, he bequeathed to her the rare skill of Maori massage, and the patience to massage deep beneath the skin and move muscles and bones and tissue to their proper places, should they be broken, torn or out of alignment.

And when he died in her arms of old age, four years ago, she was still massaging him and trying to keep his circulation going long after he became cold.

But Paraiti has a dilemma. As she closes her clinic in Ruatahuna for the day, her thoughts fly back to a request she received just before leaving Waituhi.

She was asked to take life, not to give it.

●

This is how it happened.

A week earlier, in the middle of packing for her annual trip, a thought popped into Paraiti's head: 'I think I'll ride into Gisborne and go to the pictures.' Just like that the thought came, and the more Paraiti pushed it away, the more it stuck in her mind. Truth to tell, she didn't need an excuse to go, so she made one up: she would buy some gifts for all the ladies who would be helping at her clinics on her travels. Horiana wasn't the only one, but for Horiana especially she would get her some of those Pakeha bloomers that would keep her nice and cool in the summer.

Paraiti got up at the crack of dawn, dressed in her town clothes, saddled Ataahua and set off for Gisborne. She stopped for a picnic lunch by the Taruheru River, then rode on to Gisborne and settled Ataahua in the municipal stables just across the Peel Street bridge. It was midday by the town clock when she joined the townsfolk on Gladstone Road.

Paraiti always came to Gisborne with some apprehension. Being among Pakeha was not natural for her; she felt she was crossing some great divide from one world to another. The slash of the scar across her face didn't help either; it marked her out in some sinister way. Even though these were modern times, and Pakeha liked to say that Maori and Pakeha were one people now, there were still signs of division: there were the Pakeha parts of Gisborne, particularly the palatial houses along Waterside Drive, and then there were the narrow shanty streets where the Maori lived.

Steadying her nerves, she made her way to the Regent to see what film was on. She was delighted to see that Charlie Chaplin's *The Gold Rush* was showing. She bought a ticket at the booth.

Humming to herself, Paraiti looked at the town clock again and saw that she had an hour to wait before the film began — time enough to go shopping. As she crossed Gladstone Road to Harrison Esq. Haberdashery, the latest model Packard went by with two women in it. One was a young Pakeha woman with auburn hair, of considerable beauty, and the other was a middle-aged Maori woman, probably her maid. When the Maori woman saw Paraiti, she pointed her out to her mistress.

Paraiti entered Harrison's and went over to look at the bolts of fabric. She felt she was in a magic land of laces, silks, wools, calicoes, twills and cottons. The colours were stunning — shimmering blues, glowing yellows and bright reds. A senior saleswoman appraised her as she came in and immediately approached her. 'May I help you?' she asked. There was no accompanying 'Madam' to her enquiry, but Paraiti's self-confidence had grown — and she had been to Harrison's before and she knew the kawa, the protocol:

1. Shop attendants were always supercilious but they were, sorry lady, only shop assistants, even if they were senior saleswomen.
2. She had as much right as anybody else to shop in Harrison's.
3. Her money was as good as anybody else's.

She unpinned her hat and placed it on the counter, claiming some territory. 'Why, thank you,' she said pleasantly, revealing her scar in order to intimidate the saleswoman. 'I'd like to see that bolt of cloth and that one and that one,' and she pointed to the ones that were highest in the stacks.

Meantime, Paraiti rummaged through some of the other fashionable material and accessories that were on display. By the time the saleswoman returned, she had made her selection: a variety of attractive lengths of fabric, bold, with lots of flash. She also selected a couple of pairs of bloomers with very risqué ruffles on the legs. Pleased with her purchases, Paraiti waited at the doorway for the final piece of kawa to be observed:

> 4. When the paying customer is ready to depart, the door is always opened for her.

In a happy mood, humming to herself, Paraiti made her way back to the Regent, window shopping on the way, and took her seat in the theatre. Unnoticed, the Maori maid, who had been watching Paraiti in the haberdashery, and had followed her back, took a seat a few rows back.

Paraiti loved nothing better than to sit in the dark where nobody could see her and get caught up in the fantasies on screen. She had seen Charlie Chaplin's previous movie, *The Kid*, and hoped that *The Gold Rush* would be just as good — and it was. The audience in the Regent couldn't stop laughing. Paraiti thought she would die — the tears were running down her face at the part where the starving man in the film kept looking at the little tramp and imagining seeing a nice juicy chicken. And she just about mimied herself when the little tramp was in the pivoting hut caught on the edge of a crevasse; the hut see-sawed whenever Charlie walked from one side to the other. At the end she wanted to clap and clap: Charlie Chaplin was the greatest film clown in the world. She was so glad that she had come into town.

But when she came out of the theatre into the mid-afternoon sun and saw the Maori maid standing in the sunlight like a dark presence, she felt as if somebody had just walked over her grave.

'You are Paraiti?' the maid asked. She was subservient, eyes downcast, her years weighing her down — but her words were full of purpose. 'May I trouble you for your time? I have a mistress who needs a job done. If you accept the job, you will find the price to your liking.'

Although everything in her being shouted out, 'Don't do this, turn away', Paraiti equivocated. She had always believed in fate, and it struck her that coming to Gisborne 'just like that' might not be coincidental. She found herself saying, 'Kei te pai, all right. Let me drop my parcels off at the municipal stables and then I will give your mistress an hour of my time.'

That task accomplished, the Maori servant introduced herself. 'My name is Maraea,' she said. 'My mistress is Mrs Rebecca Vickers. The Honourable Mr Vickers is currently in Europe on business. We are only recently arrived in Gisborne. Be good enough to follow me, but stay far enough back so that people do not know that we are together.'

Paraiti was immediately offended, but it was too late — she had already agreed to speak to Mrs Vickers. She followed Maraea into the Pakeha part of town. The houses on Waterside Drive, ranged along the river with willow trees greening along the banks, spoke of elegance and quality.

Maraea waved Paraiti to join her. 'The Vickers' residence is the fourth house along, the two-storey one with the rhododendron bushes and wrought-iron gate. When we arrive at the house I will go in and see if it is safe for my mistress to see you. Kindly do not approach until I signal to you with my handkerchief.'

'What have I got myself into?' Paraiti wondered. Increasingly irritated, she watched Maraea walk towards the house, disappear and, after a minute or so, return to the street and wave her handkerchief. Paraiti approached the house and was just about to enter through the gate when she heard Maraea whisper from the bushes: 'Do not come in through the front entrance, fool. Go around to the side gate, which is where such folk as you and I must enter. I will open the back door for you.'

Paraiti continued to the side gate. She opened it and walked along the gravelled pathway. A Maori gardener at work in the garden tipped his hat to her. Maraea stood at the doorway to the kitchen.

'Come in,' she urged Paraiti. 'Quickly now. And you,' she said to the gardener, 'Mrs Vickers is not pleased with the way you have trimmed the lawn. Do it again.'

Paraiti followed Maraea through a long corridor to the front of the house. The sun shone through the crystal glass of the front door. The entrance was panelled with polished wood and lined with red carpet. A tall clock ticked in an oak cabinet against one wall. A huge oval mirror hung on another wall. A small table with a visitors' book and a vase of lilies stood in the curve of the stairway to the first floor. Hanging from the ceiling was a crystal chandelier.

'Be kind enough to take off your hat,' Maraea said.

She led Paraiti up the stairs and ushered her into a back sitting-room. 'Mrs Vickers will see you soon.'

●

'Come away from the window.'

Paraiti had been in the sitting room a good ten minutes before Mrs Vickers arrived. The room showed all the trappings and accoutrements of a prosperous Pakeha merchant. The green velvet curtains were tied back with gold tassels. Antique chairs fitted with gold damask cushions were arranged around small card tables; the room was no doubt used as an after-dinner smoking-room by the gentlemen, or a place where the ladies could congregate in the afternoons to chat over cards. To one side was a fireplace, with a beautiful chaise longue in front of it. The decorations had an Oriental look — as if the Honourable and Mrs Vickers had spent some time in the East — and on the mantel above the fireplace was a photograph of a smiling couple, a young wife and her husband, standing with an Indian potentate. Electric lights in decorative glass lampshades were set into the walls, and everywhere there were mirrors. Paraiti had gravitated to the window, and was looking out at the garden below.

Turning, she immediately became disoriented; the hairs prickled on the back of her neck. In all the mirrors a young woman was reflected

— in her mid-twenties, with red hair, tall and slim, and wearing a beaded mauve dress. But which was the woman and which was her reflection? And how long had she been standing there?

On her guard, Paraiti watched as the woman approached her. She was pale, beautiful. Her hair had been tinted with henna and her skin was glazed to perfection; her eyes were green, flecked with gold, the irises large, mesmerising and open. Paraiti resisted her hypnotic gaze, and immediately the woman's irises narrowed. Then she did something perfectly strange — seductive, almost. She cupped Paraiti's chin, lifted her face and clinically observed and then touched the scar.

The act took Paraiti's breath away. Nobody except Te Teira had ever been so intimate with her. 'I was told you were ugly,' the woman said in a clipped English accent, though not without sympathy. 'But really, you are only burnt and scarred.' She withdrew her hands, but the imprint of her fingers still scalded Paraiti's skin. Then she turned, wandering through the room. 'My name is Mrs Rebecca Vickers,' she said. 'Thank you for coming. And if you have stolen anything while you have been alone in the room, it would be wise of you to put it back where it belongs before you leave.'

Paraiti bit back a sharp retort. She recognised the battle of wills that was going on, and there was nothing to stop her from leaving, except that there was something about the situation, that sense of fate again that restrained her; she would bide her time. She tried to put a background to the woman: an English girl of good family and upper-class breeding, married to a man of wealth who travelled the world; she had brought with her to New Zealand her societal expectations, including the customary control of a household run by servants. She regarded Paraiti as being in a similar position to her maid. But there was also a sense of calculation, as if she was trying to manoeuvre Paraiti into a position of subservience, even of compliance.

'What might I help you with, Mrs Vickers?' Paraiti asked. She saw that Maraea had come into the room with a small bowl of water, a handcloth and a large towel.

'Thank you, Maraea,' Mrs Vickers said. Casually, with great self-possession, she began to unbutton her dress; it fell to the floor. Her skin was whiter than white, and without blemish. Aware of her beauty, Mrs Vickers stepped out of the dress, but kept on her high heels. Although she was wearing a silk slip, Paraiti immediately saw what her artful dress had been hiding: Mrs Vickers was pregnant.

'It's very simple,' Mrs Vickers said as she removed her underwear. 'I am carrying a child. I don't want it. I want you to get rid of it.'

Her directness stunned Paraiti. Mrs Vickers was clearly a woman accustomed to getting her way. Well, two could play at that game. She asked Mrs Vickers to lie on the chaise longue and began inspecting her. 'When did you last menstruate? How many weeks have passed since then?' she asked as she felt Mrs Vickers' whare tangata — her house of birth — to ascertain the placement of the baby and the point the pregnancy had reached. The uterus had already grown to the height of the belly-button, and the skin was beginning to stretch. Paraiti concluded her inspection. Mrs Vickers liked to be direct, did she? Time then to be direct and push back.

'You are a Pakeha,' she began. 'Why have you not gone to a doctor of your own kind?'

'Of course I have consulted European doctors,' Rebecca Vickers answered, 'and much earlier than this, when I missed my period. Whatever they did to me did not work.'

'Then why have you not had further consultations with them?' Paraiti asked.

'Do not presume that I haven't done what you suggest,' Mrs Vickers responded, 'but even they failed again; they now tell me that I have gone beyond the point of no return. When Maraea saw you in the street today she thought you might offer me some hope. She told me that you Maori have ancient ways, and could get rid of it.'

'If your doctors can't perform your miracle for you,' Paraiti flared, 'don't expect me to be able to. Oh yes, I know of the herbal strategies that can lead to the termination of the pregnancy, but they work only in the first nine weeks. Some healers are able to induce the abortion by the steam bathing method and a concoction of flax and supplejack root juices. But your baby is at least twenty-four weeks grown — too late for the introduction of herbs that will make your uterus cramp and break down, so that the baby can be emptied and expelled from the womb.'

Angrily, Mrs Vickers put on her dress again. 'I knew this was a foolish notion, but Maraea told me that you were renowned for your clever hands and that, by manipulation, you could secure the result I seek.'

'And you assumed I would do it just because you asked me?' Paraiti's voice overrode Mrs Vickers. 'Why are you so intent on ridding yourself of your baby? Most women would be overjoyed to be a mother. A baby is the crown of any woman's achievement.'

When she had been inspecting Mrs Vickers the baby had *moved*, cradling against Paraiti's palms. And oh, Paraiti's heart had gone out to it.

Mrs Vickers lost her temper. 'You stupid woman,' she raged. 'That is only the case if the husband is the father. How long do you think my husband will keep me when he discovers I am pregnant with another man's child?'

So that was it.

Mrs Vickers realised she had gone too far. She reached for a silver cigarette case, opened it and took out a cigarette. Maraea lit it for her. Then, coolly, 'Are you sure there is nothing you can do for me?' she asked, inhaling.

'You are already too far gone,' Paraiti answered. 'You will have to carry the child to term.'

Mrs Vickers exhaled. Then, 'Rip it from my womb,' she said in a voice that chilled.

'That would require you to be cut open,' Paraiti flared. 'It is too dangerous and you could die, along with the baby. Even if you survived you would be scarred and carry the evidence of the operation. Your husband would know that something had happened.'

'I will pay you handsomely for your work. And for your silence.'

'It is dirty, shameful work. No person would do it.'

'What you mean is that you will not do it,' Mrs Vickers said scornfully. 'Well I will find somebody who is not as morally concerned as you are and, one way or another, I will be rid of this burden.' The smoke from her cigarette curled in the air. 'Maraea will pay you for your consultation. She will give you a cup of tea and cake before you leave.'

Maraea signed to Paraiti that the consultation was over. Just as Paraiti was leaving, she saw Mrs Vickers standing and tapping ash into an ashtray. Mrs Vickers' reflection locked eyes with Paraiti, and the room filled with eyes from all the mirrors.

'You doctors,' Mrs Vickers said. 'Pakeha or Maori, you're all the same, kei te mimi ahau ki runga ki a koutou.'

Paraiti gasped. She looked closely at Mrs Vickers' flawless skin and noted again the glaze so cleverly applied across her face. When she reached the kitchen she declined Maraea's offer of tea and cake. She wanted to get away.

'She will kill the baby,' Maraea told her, 'make no mistake about it. And if she kills her own self in doing it, well — if the baby is born, her life will be destroyed anyhow.'

You doctors, you're all the same, I will urinate on all of you.

And Paraiti asked the question, even though she already knew the answer. 'He Maori ia?'

'Yes,' Maraea answered. 'She is Maori.'

4

I t is another dawn and Paraiti drags her old bones up from sleep. She raises her hand in prayer, 'Kororia ki to ingoa tapu. Glory be to Thy holy name,' and praises God again for the gift of life and the joy of another day. What greater blessing could humankind receive than to be able to live and breathe, here, on the bright strand between earth and sky?

Five weeks have passed since Paraiti was at Ruatahuna. Horiana had just loved her bloomers; she half jested to Paraiti: 'They're so pretty, and it's such a shame to wear them under my dress, why don't I wear them on the outside?'

Pulling Kaihe after her and with Tiaki on guard, Paraiti had visited the sick, wounded and elderly of Ruatoki, Waimana and Murupara. Then, her heart lifting, she began a clinic for her patients at Te Kuiti.

It was so wonderful for Paraiti to be back among the people who had given sanctuary to her and Te Teira those many years ago. No sooner had she arrived than she was ordered by the great chief, Whaturangi, to pitch her tent close to Te Tokanganui a Noho, the great 'unification' marae, prototype for most of the later Ringatu meeting houses. 'Your dad would be cross with us if we didn't acknowledge you,' her cousin Peti growled, 'and there are enough angry ghosts floating around us as it is.' Indeed, in Paraiti's honour, a special remembrance service was held for Te Teira in the meeting house. Sitting there, within the latticed walls and with the beautiful painted kowhaiwhai rafters soaring above her, Paraiti again honoured the morehu, the loyal remnants of Te Kooti, survivors in a changing world.

Then it was down to business again. A stream of patients waited for a consultation, with Peti at the flap of the tent. A young man with a broken leg would now be able to walk, following Paraiti's skilful manipulation of his bones. An older forester, who had chopped off three fingers of his right hand, had the wounds cauterised. A child with chronic asthma would now breathe more easily if he followed the regime of herbal inhalants and exercises that Paraiti gave his anxious parents. A young girl was brought in covered in pustules; Paraiti looked after her during the night, using her poultices to draw out the pus and her soporifics to bring down the girl's fever. And if Paraiti was not able to cure all those who sought her help, at least she had tried to make them more comfortable.

From Te Kuiti, Paraiti cut across to the lands of Te Whanau a Apanui: Te Teko, Whakatane, Te Karaka and Ohiwa Harbour. More patients, more successful diagnoses and treatments, and always humour, as people laughed in the face of their illness or impending death. Like the old kuia, wasting away; when Paraiti inspected her, she was horrified, saying: 'E kui, you are all skin and bones.' To her, Paraiti had given a strong herbal painkiller, her skilful massaging hands, and the gift of a few more precious days to breathe and to praise the Lord.

Then, just after leaving her clinic at Ohiwa Habour, Paraiti had a disturbing dream. The dream was a jumble of chaotic images. A face on fire — it was her face. A ngarara bearing down on her; she took up her rifle and shot at it. As the ngarara went by, Paraiti saw a woman with auburn hair coiled within the ngarara's slithering entrails. Then Charlie Chaplin appeared — how did he get into her dream? He was in a hut and it was see-sawing on the edge of a cliff. But it wasn't Charlie

Chaplin at all — it was Paraiti herself. Suddenly, as the hut slid over the cliff, Te Teira appeared, put a hand out and pulled her out of the hut. He cupped Paraiti's chin in his hands and wiped her face clear of the scar. He did this again and again.

Paraiti woke up puzzled and anxious. What did the dream mean?

The dream gnawed at Paraiti as she travelled around the coastline from Opotiki to Omaramutu, Torere and Maraenui. Wherever she went, she performed her healing duties. As for Tiaki, Ataahua and Kaihe, they loved swimming in the sea. Paraiti took Tiaki fishing with her in a favourite lagoon. She speared a fish and let the spear sink with the fish down to the bottom. 'Kia tere,' she commanded Tiaki. Immediately he dived after the speared fish, swimming down, down, down until he was able to grasp the spear in his teeth and return to the surface.

Camping on the beach one evening, Paraiti saw an uncommonly bright star blazing across the sky. That night she had the dream again. It had changed in two respects: the auburn-haired woman had now become the ngarara, and it was a child who was caught in its slithering shape.

●

This morning, Paraiti is waiting for Tiaki to bring her breakfast. Perhaps he has gone fishing without her and will bring her back a nice silver-finned kahawai. Of course she will have to throw it back into the sea — first fish to Tangaroa — but the thought of a fish for breakfast is enticing. She leaves her tent to get some driftwood together for a fire to boil water for her manuka tea. She puts the skillet on the fire so it will be ready for Tiaki's catch.

As she is ranging along the beach, with the surf rolling in, she sees an old koroua sitting on a log in the middle of a vast expanse of sand. He is smiling at her and waving to her as if he knows her.

As soon as she sees him, Paraiti's heart bursts with pain and love.

She drops her driftwood and runs towards him like a young girl. When she gets nearer, he motions her to sit down next to him.

'Hello, daughter,' Te Teira says. 'Isn't it a lovely morning?'

Paraiti smiles at him. 'Yes, Dad.'

He closes his eyes and sniffs the sea air. 'Mmm, kei te whiti te ra, such a day brings back so many memories, daughter.' Then he looks at Paraiti again, and she can feel herself drowning in his eyes, irradiated with his love. 'You always had good hands, daughter. They can save lives and they can heal people. You know what you have to do.' Then he is gone.

After breakfast, Paraiti talks to her animals. 'Well, Tiaki, Ataahua and Kaihe, I know you are expecting us to head southward to Ngati Porou, and I know you like to visit kin at Tikitiki, Tokomaru Bay, Tolaga Bay and Whangara, but we have to cancel our travels; maybe we'll go to Ngati Porou another day. Instead, we will go straight home.'

The animals simply look at her with a puzzled expression. So? What are we waiting for? Let's get going.

Paraiti puts on her wide-brimmed hat. She packs the saddlebags, says a karakia on the beach and sprinkles sea water over her head and those of her animals. She taps Ataahua on his knees and mounts him.

It will be a long, hard ride. She wants to send a telegram from Opotiki and be at the Waioeka Gorge by nightfall, and reach Gisborne in two days' time, if all goes well.

Better get a move on. 'Me hoki matou ki te wa kainga,' she orders.

The waves thunder and spray around her as she heads inland.

5

Two days later, and Mrs Rebecca Vickers waits in the upstairs drawing room of her home on Waterside Drive.

She is smouldering with irritation. Yesterday, Maraea had brought news that Scarface had telegraphed from Opotiki to say that she was returning to Gisborne, and had a matter of mutual benefit to discuss. An appointment has been arranged for this evening.

Mrs Vickers wears her auburn hair unpinned. She is dressed in a long crimson robe. Her full and generous pregnancy is clearly showing. Her backbone has curved to make space for the baby, and all the other organs have found their places around the whare tangata.

All her attempts to end her pregnancy have failed. The last butcher left her for dead on the bathroom floor. But the baby is still alive inside her.

Lighting a cigarette, she looks out the window. The day is already beginning to wane. She rings the bell for Maraea and tells her to bring the latest edition of *The Tatler* and switch on a reading lamp. The magazine has a full-page photograph of a young film actress, Merle Oberon: rich black hair, high noble forehead, exquisite cheekbones, the neck of a swan, and skin of unsurpassed whiteness. Regarded as the quintessential English rose, Merle Oberon is the woman of her generation — looks, style and manners — on whom Rebecca Vickers has modelled her own image. Opalescent eyes blazing, she throws the magazine to the floor. Waiting for Paraiti, she broods, eyes unblinking. If she doesn't play her cards right, everything will be over. Everything.

What is Mrs Vickers' secret? She has been passing for white ever since she was a young girl of twelve. Her father was English, her mother a Maori woman he met in Auckland and promised to marry but didn't. Rather than return to her kainga, Mrs Vickers' mother instead fled to Christchurch, where her daughter was born out of wedlock. Mrs Vickers is therefore a halfcaste. In other countries where interracial relationships — or miscegenation — lead to children, those children are called, by blood quantum, halfbreed, Eurasian, mulatto or quadroon. But Mrs Vickers is more white than brown. Pigmentocracy has enabled her to blend in and thus assure for herself all the benefits of being Pakeha. So began, with her mother's connivance, her process of crossing over the colour bar.

No moral judgement should be assumed about her masquerade. Why not applaud a woman who has been able so successfully to move into the Pakeha part of town? And why not congratulate her for the huge accomplishment of catching the eye of the elderly Mr Vickers? As many other women have done before her, Mrs Vickers has parlayed her youthful sexuality to obtain matrimony and entry to high society, which she would not have obtained by pedigree. Aided by the application of an acidic nitrate, she has kept her skin glazed like porcelain; she knows full well that her white skin is her passport. She has perfected her masquerade with a long period spent in London, and an even longer period among the Raj in India, where her husband's wealth was at her disposal. She is not willing to lose everything for the sake of a moment of adulterous passion.

Mrs Vickers does not know it, but Merle Oberon is, ironically, her perfect exemplar. Born in Karachi, India, the English actress maintains her position as a famous film star only because people do not know she is Eurasian. Like Mrs Vickers, Merle Oberon, the famous English rose, also bears the taint of the tar.

Suddenly she hears footsteps. It is Maraea. 'Scarface has arrived. She is waiting for you in the parlour.'

●

Paraiti is unprepared for Mrs Vickers' appearance. One month on, pregnancy has given her a transcendent, astonishing beauty. In her crimson robe, she looks like a gorgeous katipo spider.

'You said you had a matter of mutual benefit to discuss with me,' Mrs Vickers says angrily. 'If you've come to gloat, you can get out now.'

Paraiti is exhausted from her journey. She has not detoured to Waituhi — her animals are tied up three streets away. She takes the upper hand. 'You want something from me,' she says, 'and if you agree to my terms, I will do it. I will begin the induction of your baby, tonight if you wish, and you will abort it ahead of its time.'

Mrs Vickers' eyes dilate. She turns her back on Paraiti and looks into the mirror above the fireplace, trying to mask her elation. Her reflection blazes in all the other mirrors in the room. 'Tonight? What is the method?'

'You will begin a herbal abortion. I will give you a compound which you will drink at least three times a day for the next seven days. The compound has ingredients which will bring on contractions and cause your whare tangata to collapse. By the sixth day, the compounds will affect the pito, the cord that connects your baby to your womb, and it will begin to constrict. To assist the process I will come every second evening to massage the area of the whare tangata and manipulate the baby inside. The massage will be deep, forceful and extremely painful for you. But both the compound and the massage should have the desired effect. On the seventh day I will return to physically assist your baby's expulsion from your womb.'

'Seven days?' Mrs Vickers considers the proposal. She rings the bell for the servant Maraea. 'When does Mr Vickers' ship arrive in Auckland?'

'In six days, madam,' Maraea replies.

'He will be expecting me to be there . . .' Mrs Vickers turns to Paraiti. 'You must take less time.' It is not a request; it is a command.

Paraiti stays her ground. 'Less time means more risk to you,' she answers. 'I have already accelerated the normal dosage. When the cramps begin, your body might not be able to cope with the strain. Your heart could go into arrest.'

'Less time, I say,' Mrs Vickers lashes. 'You already know how strong I am. Just rid me of my burden.'

Paraiti's head is whirling: Yes, Mrs Vickers has the stamina. She must be allowed to think that she has the victory. 'So be it,' she nods. 'I will deliver your baby on the sixth day.'

Mrs Vickers smiles with satisfaction. Then, 'I want to know if the baby will be born dead or alive,' she demands.

Paraiti realises she must be very careful about her reply. According to her calculations the pregnancy is under seven months, but the foetus should be fully viable. If so, the baby would have to survive the poisonous and dangerous ordeal as the whare tangata collapses. It could be dead before the contractions pushed it into the birth canal. Paraiti's voice quivers with emotion. 'There is every possibility that the baby will be stillborn,' she says.

Mrs Vickers looks at Maraea. 'Every possibility,' she echoes mockingly. Self-possessed, always aware, she turns to face Paraiti again.

'And why are you doing this, Scarface?' She moves with surprising swiftness, cupping Paraiti's chin with one hand and, with the other, stroking the scar that crosses her face. The touch of her hand stings.

'He Maori koe,' Paraiti answers, pulling back. 'You are a Maori.' But she can still feel Mrs Vickers probing her soul, and she warns her, 'Kia tupato, tuahine. Be careful. What I am proposing to do is against the law. You push me and I will change my mind.'

The threat of withdrawal has the desired effect. Mrs Vickers blinks and steps back. But she is soon on the offensive again. 'You mentioned your terms. What do you want, Scarface?'

It is now or never. 'I will not require payment for my services,' Paraiti says quickly. 'You will not understand this, Mrs Vickers, but my purpose is to save lives, not to take life away. Whether the baby is dead or alive, I will keep it.'

'What are you up to?' Mrs Vickers asks. 'Wait here while I consider.'

Paraiti watches as Mrs Vickers and Maraea leave the room. She hears them talking in low voices. When they return, Mrs Vickers mocks, 'I had not realised that your motives would be so humanitarian, but I agree to your request. What option do I have? You hold all the cards. I should have known you wouldn't want blood money to go with it. But I warn you, Paraiti, if the baby is alive, take it quickly for I would soon murder it. Now let us begin the treatment.'

Asking Maraea to bring up the saddlebags containing her medicines, Paraiti instructs both women on the dosage and its frequency. She measures out the first dose and administers it. Self-confident though she is, Mrs Vickers' eyes show alarm. Her face increases in pallor; after all, it is a poison that is being administered to her. Following the dose, Paraiti begins to massage Mrs Vickers. The massage is light at first and Mrs Vickers sighs and relaxes into it. 'This is not so difficult to cope with,' she laughs. But then Paraiti goes deeper, stronger, faster — above, around and upon the mound of the whare tangata. Soon, sweat starts to pop out on Mrs Vickers' forehead and she groans, 'No, please, enough, no.' For half an hour Paraiti keeps up the massage, her eyes dark and her face grim, until Mrs Vickers starts to scream with the pain.

Paraiti stops. Mrs Vickers moans; she can feel the after-effects of Paraiti's manipulations rippling within her womb.

But the massage isn't over.

Paraiti administers a hard, shocking series of chops with her hands on and around the baby within the whare tangata, then applies relentless pressure on the baby. *Please child, forgive me, but this is the only way.* She can sense the baby beneath her hands, fighting the unbearable pain — and Mrs Vickers screams and loses consciousness.

'Every second day, this?' Maraea asks, horrified.

'Yes,' Paraiti answers. 'Meantime, make sure your mistress drinks the compound. This regime is the only way to achieve the abortion on the sixth day. Under no circumstances can we slow or halt the procedure.'

It is time for Paraiti to leave. Just as she does so, Mrs Vickers revives and, exhausted, speaks to her. 'You and I, Scarface, we are not so dissimilar. You wear your scar where people can see it. I wear mine where they can't. Our lives have both been influenced by them. Me pera maua.'

Paraiti ponders her words, and then nods in reluctant agreement. 'I can find my own way out,' she says. She walks down the stairs, along the corridor to the side door. As she walks down the pathway and closes the gate behind her, she is aware that Mrs Vickers is watching her go. She continues along Waterside Drive and, when she is out of sight of the house, her legs fail her and she collapses into the shadows. 'Oh, child, forgive me for the pain I have done to you tonight.'

My purpose is to save lives, Mrs Vickers, not take them away.

She hears panting and sees that Tiaki has joined her; he licks her face. In the distance, tied to a fence, are Ataahua and Kaihe. Sighing to herself, Paraiti joins her animals. They could be home by dawn.

'I have gambled tonight,' she says to Tiaki as she mounts Ataahua. 'I have played a game of life and death. Let us pray that I will win.'

Together they fade in and out of the streetlights and, finally, into the comforting dark beyond the town.

6

Normally, Paraiti would have spent the rest of her haerenga on a circuit of the villages closest to Waituhi. The old woman with a dog, horse and mule are familiar sights among the Ringatu faithful in Turanga, which the Pakeha have renamed Poverty Bay.

Paraiti would have travelled throughout the lands of Te Whanau a Kai, Te Aitanga a Mahaki, Tai Manuhiri and Rongowhakaata. Wherever the Ringatu festivals take place, there you would have found her. Where the faithful gather to sing, pray and praise God, there she would be also: Waihirere, Puha, Mangatu, Rangatira, Waioeka, Awapuni, Muriwai and many other local marae. Still avoiding te rori Pakeha, the Pakeha road, she would instead have ridden the old trails along the foothills or rivers, the unseen roads that crisscross the plains like a spider's web.

But for six days, Paraiti remains in Waituhi, venturing only every second day to Gisborne, and returning at midnight. 'Where is Scarface?' her people ask, puzzled at this change in her routine. 'Is she ill? What will happen to us if she is unable to visit this year?' And some, worried, come to Waituhi to knock on the door of her kauta. 'Are you all right, takuta?'

When they are patiently told that everything is kei te pai and that she is only delayed, they leave.

Even so, Paraiti decides to make an appearance at a Ringatu hui at Takipu, the large meeting house at Te Karaka, so that the people will see she's still alive and kicking. Takipu is so beautiful that Paraiti cannot help but be grateful that her whakapapa connects her to such a glorious world.

The hui incorporates a kohatu ceremony, an unveiling of the headstone of a brother Ringatu healer, Paora, who died a year ago. The obelisk, the final token of aroha, is polished granite, gleaming in the sun. It is a sign of the love for a rangatira. As Paraiti joins the local iwi, weeping, around the obelisk, she reflects on the fragility of life. 'Not many of us morehu left,' she thinks to herself.

Afterwards, she spends some time talking to Paora's widow, Tereina. 'It was a beautiful unveiling for a beautiful man,' she says.

'Ae,' Tereina replies. 'A woman must have a good man at least once in her lifetime and I was lucky, he was the best.' Tereina smiles at the memory. 'The men may be the leaders, but when they die, it is the women who become the guardians of the land and the future.'

Returning to Waituhi, Paraiti cannot shake off Tereina's comment about having a man in her life. She has always been alone with her animals, unloved by any man except her beloved father. Would things have been different if she had not been scarred?

Her mood deepens as she thinks of all the changes she has observed in her travels. Since she and her father saw the ngarara, the marks of the new civilisation have proliferated across the land. New highways and roads. More sheep and cattle farms. Where once there was a swingbridge there is now a two-lane bridge across the river. And although the old Maori tracks are still there, many of them have barbed-wire fences across them, necessitating a detour until a gate is found. On the gate is always a padlock and a sign that says 'Private Land. Tresspassers will be prosecuted. Keep out.'

The changes are always noted by the travellers of the tracks and passed on to other travellers, 'Kia tupato, beware,' because, sometimes, horses or children can be ensnared in the coils of barbed wire discarded in the bush after the fences have been built. Paraiti has sewn up many wounds inflicted by barbed wire as pighunters and foresters have rushed after prey in the half light of darkness.

So the travellers keep themselves up to date with the death of Maori country. And Paraiti suddenly recalls Mrs Vickers' words. *You wear your scar where people can see it. I wear mine where they can't.*

Of all the changes wreaked by civilisation, it is the spiritual changes that are the worst. The ngarara is not only physical; it has already infiltrated and invaded the moral world that Paraiti has always tried to protect. She cannot but compare Mrs Vickers' situation to that of the young girl in Ruatahuna — what was her name again, Florence? — who had lost three babies while they were still in the womb. In one case, the baby is strongly desired; in the other, unwanted.

Perhaps the marks that really matter are, indeed, the ones that can't be seen.

●

How Paraiti manages to get through the next six days, she will never know. She prays constantly, morning, noon and night, her karakia unceasing and seamless. All that sustains her as she hastens to Waterside Drive and her rendezvous with Mrs Vickers is her immense faith, and the words of her father, 'You know what you have to do.'

But every second evening, when Maraea meets her at the side door, 'Come in, quickly, before you are seen,' Paraiti feels sick to her stomach that all her efforts might be for nought — that, instead of saving the baby, she will be complicit in its death. And every time she administers the herbal compound, following it up with forceful massaging, and then the rapid blows to the womb, she realises that her anxiety must be as nothing when compared to that of the baby in the womb.

What must it be like to be in the house of birth, a whare meant to nurture and sustain, undergoing the trauma as its walls and roof are caving in? And in that environment, with stitched tukutuku ripping apart, kowhaiwhai panels cracking, and the destruction of all the whakapapa contained therein, what must it be like for the baby? Where can it go when the poutokomanawa begins to collapse and the poisons begin to flood through the placenta that feeds it? Even when fighting back, how can it know that even this is anticipated and is part of its brutal eviction?

'Forgive me, child, oh forgive me,' Paraiti whispers as she maintains the treatment. Ironically, Mrs Vickers' own strength and stamina are working in the baby's favour.

And on the sixth evening, when Mrs Vickers, groaning in pain, cries out, 'Now, Scarface, do your work and rid me of this child,' Paraiti plays her trump.

She has been stalling for time. 'Your cervix has not dilated sufficiently,' she says to Mrs Vickers. 'The door of the whare tangata is not wide enough to enable the baby's delivery.' Paraiti has not increased the dosage, nor the massage therapy; every hour increases the chances of the baby's survival. Turning a deaf ear to Mrs Vickers' torrent of curses, Paraiti tells her, 'I will do it tomorrow night.'

'Kororia ki to ingoa tapu,' she prays to the evening sky and all throughout the next day. Her animals, sensing her anxiety, honour her fervency with barks, whinnies and brays of their own; otherwise, they stand and wait in silence and on good behaviour.

●

'You planned this delay all along,' Mrs Vickers seethes. 'Well, two can play at that game, Scarface.'

The final treatment has forced her waters to break. The birth has begun. The contractions are coming strongly — and the baby has slipped from the whare tangata into the birth canal.

Paraiti ignores the accusation. 'Your trial will soon be over,' she answers, 'and it will be advisable for you to focus on the difficulties ahead. A normal birth is difficult enough. One that has been induced as forcefully as this, and before time, is more so.'

Yes, Mrs Vickers has stamina all right but, even so, she is being truly tested. She is dressed in a white slip, the cloth already stained at her thighs. Her skin shines with a film of sweat.

'How do you wish to give birth, Mrs Vickers?' Paraiti asks. 'The Maori way or the Pakeha way?' She knows the question has a hint of insolence about it but, after all, Mrs Vickers has Maori ancestry and it needs to be asked. Although the Pakeha position is prone, unnatural, Paraiti assumes that this is the way Mrs Vickers would wish the baby to be delivered. Her answer, however, surprises Paraiti.

'My mother has prepared a place so that I can deliver the Maori way,' she says. 'If it was good enough for her illegitimate child, it is good enough for mine.'

Her mother?

Paraiti realises that Mrs Vickers is talking about Maraea. 'Ki a koe?' she asks Maraea, and she looks at the older woman to affirm the relationship.

Maraea averts her eyes but nods her head briefly. 'Yes, I am Rebecca's mother. But I never thought the pathway would lead to this, Scarface, believe me.'

There is no resemblance at all. One is old, dark, indecisive; the other young, fair, purposeful. What kind of unholy relationship, what kind of charade is this between daughter and mother?

Leading the way, and supporting her daughter as she goes, Maraea beckons Paraiti down the circular stairs and then a further set of steps to a small cellar. She switches on a light and Paraiti sees that Maraea has done her work well. Two hand posts have been dug into the clay, and beneath the place where Mrs Vickers will squat are clean cotton blankets and a swaddling cloth to wrap the baby in.

With a cry of relief, Mrs Vickers shrugs off her slip and, naked, takes her place between the posts in a squatting position, thighs apart. Her pendulous breasts are already leaking with milk. 'No, I won't need those,' she says to Maraea, refusing the thongs that her mother wants to bind her hands with. 'Do your work, Scarface,' she pants, 'and make it quick.'

Maraea has already taken a position behind her, supporting her.

'Massage your daughter,' Paraiti commands. 'Press hard on her lower abdomen and whare tangata so that the baby is prompted to move further downward.'

The whare tangata is collapsing. But there is a heartbeat — faint, but a sign — to reveal that the baby still lives. 'I am here, child,' Paraiti whispers. 'Kia tere, come quickly now.' She takes her own position, facing Mrs Vickers, and presses her knees against her chest.

'You will pay for this,' she says. And suddenly her face is in rictus. She takes a deep breath, her mouth opening in surprise, 'Oh.'

Paraiti places her hands on Mrs Vickers' swollen belly. She feels the baby beneath, as it pushes head first against the birth opening. Paraiti's manipulation is firm and vigorous as she presses and hastens the baby on its way. The contractions are rippling, stronger and stronger, and the first fluids stream from the vagina as the doorway proudly begins to open.

'Now, bear down,' Paraiti orders.

Mrs Vickers does not flail the air. Her face constricts and she arches her neck with a hiss. With a gush of blood, undulation after undulation, the baby slides out, head followed by shoulders, body and limbs, into the world. The baby is dark-skinned with wet, matted red hair.

'A girl,' Paraiti whispers in awe. 'Haere mai, e hine, ki te Ao o Tane. Welcome, child, to the world of humankind.'

Quickly, she cradles her, clearing her face of mucus, ready to give her the first breath of life.

'No,' Mrs Vickers instructs. 'Let it die.'

Paraiti does not heed her. Maraea is weeping, restraining Mrs Vickers as Paraiti clears the baby's mouth and massages her chest. Immediately, she starts to wail. Her eyes open. They are green, shining, angry.

Mrs Vickers falls back, exhausted. She doesn't even look at her daughter.

Paraiti cuts the umbilical cord and ties it with flax. She places the child at Mrs Vickers' breast.

Mrs Vickers looks at Paraiti. 'You broke your agreement to deliver me in six days. I now break mine. This child has no future. Get out.'

●

'Have I failed?'

Paraiti's faith makes her keep watch by the sickle moon on the house of Mrs Vickers. Around two o'clock in the morning, she sees Mrs Vickers and Maraea getting into the Packard.

Earlier, when Maraea showed Paraiti to the door, she said, 'Rebecca will not kill the baby in this house. She wants to, but I have convinced her of the spiritual consequences of such an act — of having a child ghost destroy the calm of her life. But she will get rid of it. Keep watch and follow closely after us.'

'E Tiaki,' Paraiti tells her dog, 'kia tere. Follow.' Keeping to the shadows, Tiaki slinks silently in pursuit. Paraiti follows after on Ataahua.

The Packard is travelling fast. Ataahua is at the gallop. Even so, Paraiti has trouble keeping up and has to rely on Tiaki to run ahead, keep watch, return to show Ataahua the way, and run ahead again. Nevertheless, together they manage to hold on to the thin thread of pursuit, and when Paraiti reaches Roebuck Road, she sees the Packard parked on the bridge overlooking the river.

On the other side of the bridge is a small Maori settlement.

Paraiti quickly dismounts and watches from the darkness.

Mrs Vickers gets out of the car and takes a sack from the back seat. She moves very slowly and painfully but with determination. Paraiti hears a thin wail from within the sack. Her eyes prick with tears. She cannot believe Mrs Vickers intends to throw the sack in the river.

But Maraea is objecting. She struggles with her daughter saying, 'Kaore, daughter, no.' Mrs Vickers slaps her and she falls to the ground. Then, taking up the sack, she throws it over the bridge as cavalierly as if she is drowning kittens.

'Aue, e hine,' Paraiti cries.

She must wait until the car turns and makes its way back to Waterside Drive. Once it has gone past her hiding place she runs to the bridge to look over. The sack is floating away on the dark river; it won't be too long before it sinks. 'Haere atu,' she yells to Tiaki. She points at the sack in the river and he jumps off the bridge and splashes into the water.

Paraiti's heart is beating as she slips and slides down to the river's edge. She can hear the thin wail of the child again. 'Kia tere, kia tere!' she urges Tiaki. The sack is becoming waterlogged and it is sinking. 'Quick, Tiaki, quick.'

He is too late. The sack disappears under the water.

With a yelp, Tiaki dives for it — has not his mistress taught him at a favoured lagoon to bring back speared fish from the sea? The depths of the river are dark, so dark. But something flicks across his nose, a trailing piece of twine from the sack as it goes deeper, and he lunges—

Tiaki breaks out of the water. In his teeth, he has the sack. 'He kuri pai!' Paraiti calls to him, 'Good dog. Hoki mai ki ahau. Bring the baby to me.'

Her usually clever fingers are so clumsy! They take so long to untie the knot. 'Do your work quickly, fingers, quickly.'

And, oh, the baby is so still, with the tinge of blue on her skin. She already has the waxen sheen of death upon her. 'Move quickly, hands, you have always healed, always saved lives. Give warmth to the child, massage the small heart and body to beat again and to bring the water up from her lungs. Quickly, hands, quickly. And now—'

Paraiti holds the baby by the ankles and, praying again, gives the child a mighty slap on her tiny bottom.

The heart begins to pump, the lungs expel the water and the baby yells, spraying water out of her mouth. She tries to draw breath but starts to cough; that's good, as she will get rid of all the water from her lungs. Very soon she is breathing and crying, and Paraiti continues to rub her down, increasing her body warmth. Tiaki noses in to see what she is doing. He whimpers with love and licks her.

'Oh, pae kare,' Paraiti says to herself, 'Oh, thank God.' She takes a moment to calm down. Then she addresses the baby, 'I will call you Waiputa,' she says. 'Born of water.' She sprinkles her head with water to bless her.

Waiputa is already nuzzling Paraiti's breasts. 'You're not going to have any luck with those old dugs,' Paraiti tells her. 'I better find you a wet nurse.' She looks across the river at the Maori settlement; there's bound to be some younger woman there, breastfeeding her own child, who owes Paraiti a favour and won't mind suckling another child.

As for the future? Paraiti smiles to herself. 'What a menagerie we will make, Waiputa! A scar-faced woman, two old nags, a pig dog and you.'

Others had begun their lives with less.

7

S even years later.

Time has been kind to Paraiti. Although her eyesight has dimmed a little, her memory is as sharp as ever, her medical skills intact, and her hands still do their blessed work. Tiaki has grown a bit greyer and is not as formidable a hunter in the forest as he used to be; instead of hunting a second pigeon he sometimes nips the first one on a wing so that it can't fly too far and, when Paraiti releases it, sneakily, that is the same one he brings back. Both Ataahua and Kaihe are casting a keen eye on the pasture across the road where they can be retired to live out the rest of their years. Time for some other young colt and mule to take over.

This morning Paraiti woke as usual at dawn, said her karakia, performed her ablutions, packed the saddlebags and set off down the road. She still makes her annual haerenga and, in the year 1936, she is on her way to a hui at Te Mana o Turanga, Whakato Marae, Manutuke, the birthplace of the prophet Te Kooti. Oh, how she loves that meeting house! So full of carvings and stories of the people. Whenever she visits, it is like the past comes to life before her.

And she is so looking forward to the hui, too. There are two major thanksgiving festivals in the annual Ringatu calendar: one is held on

1 June, coinciding with the beginning of the Maori New Year, when the mara tapu is planted to commemorate God's promise of salvation to all humankind; the other is held on 1 November, the celebration of the Passover, established by the prophet Te Kooti according to Exodus 40:2: 'Hei tera tuatahi o te marama tuatahi koe, whakaara ai te tapenakara o te teneti o te whakaminenga.'

The tapu is lifted from the sacred garden and what has been planted on 1 June is harvested — symbolic of the resurrection of Christ. In this ceremony of 'The Lifting of the First Fruits', the people make a commitment for the next six months to walk in righteousness.

Paraiti usually travels by the side of the Pakeha roads now. Many of the great Maori trails are fenced off, and the last time she travelled on Rua's Track, she had trouble hanging on when she was negotiating the steepest part. But she still grumbles about the ways that civilisation is advancing through the world, and she is always pointing out more of its marks.

She comes to the fork of the road where roadmen have been constructing a combined road and rail bridge. She's never seen one quite like it. The road has been made of a black and sticky material. Tiaki sniffs at it and growls. Ataahua and Kaihe stand patiently waiting for the order to move across.

'It might be like the Red Sea,' Paraiti mutters. 'We could be halfway and next minute, aue, the waves will come over us.'

'No it won't, Nan,' a young voice says. 'It's called tarseal. Come on, there's no traffic. Let's cross now.'

Riding Kaihe is a pretty young girl, dark, with auburn hair. Paraiti has an assistant now, a whangai daughter, Waiputa. Waiputa now fills her waning years. She is someone to love; the new seed for the future, blossoming from Paraiti's old life. In turn, Waiputa is someone who loves her matua. They make a good team, the scarred one and the unscarred one.

'Tarseal, eh?' Paraiti answers. 'You're learning lots of big words at that school of yours.'

She pulls Kaihe across the black river. Aue, motorised traffic is faster than a horse and an old mule. It can come out of nowhere and is onto you before you know it. Roaring across the bridge like a ngarara comes a huge sheep truck and trailer.

'Quickly, Nan,' Waiputa says. 'We have to get to the other side of the road.'

But Paraiti knows how fast she can go. Quick? She is already at quick. There's nothing to do except face the ngarara. 'E tu,' she says to Ataahua and Kaihe. Together, they turn to the oncoming monster. Paraiti reaches for her rifle.

The truck driver signals to her, 'Get off the road,' and then slams on the brakes. The truck squeals to a halt, its trailer rattling, wheezing, collapsing before the old woman and her whangai daughter. The driver swears and starts to open the door. But when he sees the old, greying dog snarling and the little red-haired girl baring her teeth, he shuts it again, quick and lively. 'Stupid old woman,' he yells at Paraiti as he drives his truck around them.

Paraiti gets to the other side of the road. Waiputa looks at her and wags a finger. 'Bad girl, Nan. We could have been killed.'

'I know,' Paraiti answers. 'And I realise it was just a truck. But you know, in the old days, I would have shot it.'

Paraiti peers at the sun and begins to laugh and laugh. Then, looking at the road ahead she pulls down her sunhat and says to Waiputa, Tiaki, Ataahua and Kaihe:

'Looks like we're just going to have to last forever.'

WHITE LIES
CAST AND
CREW LIST

SOUTH PACIFIC
PICTURES LTD

SOUTH PACIFIC PICTURES IN ASSOCIATION WITH
THE NEW ZEALAND FILM COMMISSION
AND NEW ZEALAND ON AIR

WHITE LIES

WHIRIMAKO BLACK
RACHEL HOUSE
ANTONIA PREBBLE

WRITTEN & DIRECTED BY
DANA ROTBERG

PRODUCERS
JOHN BARNETT
CHRIS HAMPSON

FROM THE NOVELLA *MEDICINE WOMAN*
BY WITI IHIMAERA

CINEMATOGRAPHY
ALUN BOLLINGER

EDITOR
PAUL SUTORIUS

MUSIC
JOHN PSATHAS

DESIGN
TRACEY COLLINS

LINE PRODUCER
CATHERINE MADIGAN

SOUND DESIGN
JAMES HAYDAY

CASTING
CHRISTINA ASHER

Paraiti	WHIRIMAKO BLACK
Maraea	RACHEL HOUSE
Rebecca	ANTONIA PREBBLE
Horiana	NANCY BRUNNING
Aroha	TE WAIMARIE KESSELL
Wirepa	KOHUORANGI TAWHARA
Hospital Matron	ELIZABETH HAWTHORNE
Young Paraiti	TE AHUREI RAKURAKU
Paraiti's Grandfather	MAHURI OTE RANGI TRAINOR TAIT
Soldiers	STEVE MCQUILLAN
	KYLE PRYOR
	GEORGE SMITH Snr
	GEORGE SMITH Jnr
	JONATHAN TORKINGTON
Horiana's Grandchild	RAWIRI WAIARIKI
Pirihimana	TE WHENUA TE KURAPA
Woman with Bad Leg	TANGIORA TAWHARA
Limping Girl	VANESSA PARAKI
Chemist	PHIL PELETON
Pharmacy Worker	JUANITA HEPI
Girl at Cinema	RINA KENOVIĆ
Woman at Cinema	KATE STALKER
Children at Cinema	GRIFFIN GOUGH STALKER
	TESS GOUGH STALKER
Gardener	WILLIAM DAVIS
Uncle Jim	JIM WHITE
Asthmatic Boy	TE UREWERA KAPEA-RUA
European Nurse	SOPHIE HAMBLETON
Aroha's Uncle	MELVIN TE WANI
Maori Nurse	PATRICIA VICHMAN
Hospital Orderly	TIM COOPER
Rebecca's Baby	DEIZHON MANAWANUI KING
Mr Vickers' Employee	JON BRAZIER
Rebecca's Child	TE AHUMAIRANGI BRIDIE POTTS
Script Editor	MICHAEL DONNELLY
1st Assistant Director	HAMISH GOUGH
Location Manager	CHARLOTTE GARDNER
On Set Art Director	DAVIN VOOT
Off Set Art Director	MILTON CANDISH
Make-Up/Hair Supervisor	ABBY COLLINS
Gaffer	GILLY LAWRENCE
Key Grip	TERRY JOOSTEN
Sound Recordist	ADAM MARTIN
Kaitiaki	NGAMARU RAERINO
Cultural Advisor	KARARAINA RANGIHAU
Iwi Liason	WHITIAUA ROPITINI
Advisor to the Director	TANGIORA TAWHARA
Script Supervisor	HAYLEY ABBOTT
Focus Puller	BRADLEY WILLEMSE
2nd Assistant Camera	ALYSSA KATH

Video Split	NINA WELLS
Best Boy	BEN CORLETT
Generator Operator	STEVE JOYCE
Lighting Assistant	MANA LAWRENCE
Assistant Grip	TIM WATSON
Additional Grips	TOBY CONWAY
	ROAN LEWISHAM
Boom Operators	SAM GOOD
	NIKORA EDWARDS
2nd Assistant Directors	KATIE TATE
	CATHERINE BENNETTO
3rd Assistant Director	LANCE MCMINN
Trainee Director	KARARAINA RANGIHAU
Animal Trainers	ANIMALS ON Q
Dog Trainer	KIM LUX
Horse Trainer	ROSIE MILES
Animal Wranglers	MARLON HART
	JULIE WHIU
Art Department Coordinator	KATE OLIVE
Set Decorator	ANITA DEMPSEY
Set Dresser	SETU LIO
Assistant Set Dresser	LEAH MIZRAHI
Props Master/Standby Props	NICK WILLIAMS
Greens	SAM HOLLYER
Graphics	LISA RUSHWORTH
Art Assistant	JESSICA LEIJH
Additional Art Assistant	CALUM MACMILLAN
Scenic Artist	PAUL NY
Vehicle Wrangler	IAN GOLDINGHAM
Armourer	PETER 'GUNNER' ASHFORD
Special Effects	FILM EFFECTS LTD
Special Effects Technicians	SVEN HARRENS
	ALASTAIR VARDY
Construction Manager	NIK NOVIS
Carpenters	MERV LAMBERT
	JASON JOHNSON
Assistant Costume Designer	KIRI RAINEY
Costume Standby	CARMEL RATA
Costume Assistant/Dresser	EMMA RANSLEY
Pattern Cutter	MITCH ANDREWS
Costume Machinist	KIRSTY MCLAY
Make-Up/Prosthetics Artist	YOLANDA BARTRAM
Make-Up & Hair Artist	VEE GULLIVER
Facial Prosthetics Designer	ANDREW BEATTIE
Belly Prosthetics	MAIN REACTOR
Acting Coach	STEPHANIE WILKIN
Production Coordinator	MICHELLE LEAITY
Production Secretary	SARAH BANASIAK
Production Runner	AIMEE RUSSELL
Additional Production Assistant	CHARLOTTE PARSON
Chaperone	DEBORAH LANE

Midwife	ABBY CLARK
Production Accountant	SUSIE BUTLER
Post Production Accountant	ESTHER SCHMIDT
Additional Location Manager	JACOB MCINTYRE
Location Assistant	NINA BARTLETT
Unit Manager	DUN
Unit Assistant	ANDREW D'ALMEIDA
Catering	MARVEL CATERING
Safety Supervisor	ROBERT 'GIBBO' GIBSON
Assistant Editor	SHAILESH PRAJAPATI
Stunt Coordinator/Performer	STEVE MCQUILLAN
Stunt Performer	KYLE PRYOR
Stunt Double Rider	RICHARD WHITE

RUATAHUNA CREW

Art Assistants	GRAHAM RANGIHAU
	BONNEY SMITH
	ROGER WHITE
Horse Wrangler	PAREHUIA EPARAIMA
Production Runners	HINEMA RUREHE
	JOHN BIRRELL
Location Assistants	JIM WHITE
	MERIANN WHITE
	MAHURI OTE RANGI TRAINOR TAIT
	RICHARD WHITE
	TE KIATO 'TK' MOREHU
Security	PETER TIMOTI
	STEVE PENWRIGHT
Catering	MERIANN WHITE
	THE WHITE FAMILY
	OPUTAO MARAE
2nd Unit Camera	DJ STIPSEN
2nd Unit Focus Pullers	SAM MATTHEWS
	LEE ALLISON
Security	PARAGON NZ
Script Development	TIM BALME
	JO JOHNSON
Maori Language Translations	KARARAINA RANGIHAU
	WHITIAUA ROPITINI
	TANGIORA TAWHARA
	RANGITUNOA BLACK
Post Production	IMAGES & SOUND LTD
Post Production Supervisor	GRANT BAKER
Post Production Coordinator	ANNA RANDALL
DI Conform/Titles	ANDREW MORTIMER
Digital Intermediate Colourist	PAUL LEAR

Assistant Colourist	ALANA COTTON
Engineering	ANDREW ROSS
VFX	ANDREW MORTIMER
	BRENTON CUMBERPATCH
	CARLOS PURCELL
	DAVID MYLES
Digital Cinema Package	TRISTAN SIMPSON
Film Output	WETA DIGITAL
Film Recording Manager	PETE WILLIAMS
Film Recording Supervisor	NICK BOOTH
Film Recording Technician	DANIEL ASHTON
Film Laboratory Services	PARK ROAD POST PRODUCTION
Sound Post Production	IMAGES&SOUND LTD
Supervising Sound Editor	STEVE FINNIGAN
Dialogue Editor	CHRIS SINCLAIR
Sound Effects Editor	JAMES HAYDAY
ADR Recordist	STEVE FINNIGAN
Sound Mixing Studio	DIGIPOST LTD
Re Recording Mixer	CHRIS SINCLAIR
Foley Artist	JONATHAN BRUCE
Foley Engineer	GARETH VAN NIEKERK
Dolby Consultant	BRUCE EMERY

ADR LOOP GROUP

ANGELINE VAIKE	ANNIE TE MOANA
GEOFFREY DOLAN	GREG JOHNSON
GRIFFIN GOUGH STALKER	JAROME HENERE-SAMUELS
KAHLEE HENARE-SAMUELS	KARARAINA RANGIHAU
KATARAINA WIAPO	KATE STALKER
KIRK TORRANCE	NARELLE AHRENS
POMARE TAWHAI	POTAUA HOTENE
RAYMOND BRUCE HOPKINS	STEPHEN HALL
TAMAKAIMOANA HUNE	TE RUKI TE MOANA
TESS GOUGH STALKER	TUMANAWA TAWHAI

Legal and Business Affairs	JESSICA WISEMAN
	HEATHER AH YEN
Financial Controller	TANIA BETTANY
Publicist & EPK	TAMAR MÜNCH
Stills Photographer	TODD EYRE
Trailers	JAMES BROOKMAN

THE PRODUCERS WISH TO THANK
OPUTAO MARAE
TE UMUROA MARAE
THE PEOPLE OF RUATAHUNA VALLEY
HIGHWIC & ALBERTON — NZ HISTORIC PLACES TRUST PROPERTIES

THE PRODUCTION GRATEFULLY ACKNOWLEDGES THE
SUPPORT, ADVICE AND ASSISTANCE OF
TE HAAHI RINGATU O RUATAHUNA

SPECIAL THANKS TO

ROSA BOSCH
RICHARD & MERIANN WHITE
MOANA MANIAPOTO
JOE MCCLUTCHIE
ANI PRIP
HINEIRA WOODARD
MINITA PRIP
CALUM MACMILLAN
LEANNE POOLEY
DIANNE TAYLOR
HINEWAI MACMANUS
JON ARVIDSON
JOHN MACDERMOTT
GERALD LOPEZ
ESTHER AMMANN
KATHLEEN BENNETT

FAY CLARK
MERCEDES HOPE
ANNETTE MASON
CLAIRE STAFFORD
TRISH HOLLOWAY
CHARLES DIVINS
PATY AGUIRE
SEAN PUMFLEET
LEON CONSTANTINER
WARWICK GOUGH
JIM BUTTERWORTH
CHRIS MEADE
RINA KENOVIĆ
JULIO DIAZ
MOOMOO THE DOG

PRODUCED WITH THE ASSISTANCE OF
THE DEPARTMENT OF CONSERVATION,
TE UREWERA WHIRINAKI OFFICE
TE PAPA ATAWHAI, NEW ZEALAND

Original Music Composed by	JOHN PSATHAS
Performed by	RICHARD NUNNS Taonga Puoro
	EMMA SAYERS Pianist
	SASHA GACHENKO Bass
	MATT CAVE Bass
	ROWAN PRIOR Cello
	PAUL MITCHELL Cello
	KONSTANZE ARTMANN Viola
	IRINA ANDREEVA Viola
	KATE OSWIN Violin
	MATTHEW ROSS Violin
Score Recording Engineer & Mixer	GRAHAM KENNEDY
Assistant Score Recording Engineer	CHRIS KEOGH

Music Production Supervisor   INGE RADEMEYER
Typesetting   BEN WOODS
Composer's Assistant   BRIAR PRASTITI

THANKS TO
VICTORIA UNIVERSITY OF WELLINGTON
NEW ZEALAND SCHOOL OF MUSIC
RADIO NEW ZEALAND

'MELODIC INSTRUMENT 2'
WRITTEN & PERFORMED BY RICHARD NUNNS
COURTESY OF RATTLE RECORDS

Camera and Lenses   QUEENSTOWN CAMERAS

Insurance   CROMBIE LOCKWOOD (NZ) LTD
                              MARTIN TRENDALL

THIS FILM WAS MADE WITH ASSISTANCE FROM
THE SCREEN PRODUCTION INCENTIVE FUND

BASED ON THE NOVELLA *MEDICINE WOMAN*
BY WITI IHIMAERA
FROM THE COLLECTION *ASK THE POSTS OF THE HOUSE*
PUBLISHED BY REED BOOKS

MADE BY NEW ZEALAND

FILMED ON LOCATION IN NEW ZEALAND
IN TE UREWERA, RUATAHUNA, LAKE WAIKAREMOANA AND
AUCKLAND